Lincoln Christian College
W9-BUT-297

Take Her, Mr. Wesley

Other Books by John W. Drakeford

Made for Each Other
Children of Doom
Forbidden Love
Games Husbands and Wives Play
This Insanity Called Love
Farewell to the Lonely Crowd
The Awesome Power of the Listening Ear
Integrity Therapy
The Great Sex Swindle
Marriage Duet or Discord
Psychology in Search of a Soul
Red Blueprint for the World
Counseling for Church Leaders

Take Her, Mr. Wesley

John W. Drakeford

WORD BOOKS, PUBLISHER
Waco, Texas

Take Her, Mr. Wesley by John Drakeford

Library of Congress catalog card number 72-84158

Printed in the United States of America

Dedicated to

Mrs. John H. Warnick
Methodist Historical Librarian
Southern Methodist University

whose contagious spirit
encouraged my study of John Wesley

Contents

Take Her, Mr. Wesley

1.

If I Had Twenty Sons

February 6, 1736

THE TWO MEN climbed down the ladder into the ship's cutter where the sailors sat with oars upright in naval precision. Taking their seats, the older man nodded his permission to the boatswain who gave the order that got them under way. Rhythmically dipping oars sent the bow of the boat slicing through the water, launching wavelets which followed each other like ranks of guardsmen on parade.

The man who had given the signal wore the uniform of a British army officer. His scarlet tunic tailored from the finest material was shaped in just the right manner to display the buff waistcoat edged with silver lace. The tunic itself was laced with gold, and it had a gold knot on the right shoulder through which passed a crimson sash. His cocked hat could not hide the high forehead above his finely arched eyebrows. An elaborately curled wig framed his face.

The shorter man at his side was handsome but not in the autocratic manner of his companion. About him there hovered a subtle ethereal air. His clothes, although very neatly worn, were of less than the best quality. Two white tabs at his throat relieved the blackness of his clerical gown. He wore no wig. Auburn hair hung around a deathly white face from which projected a large nose, no real aid to his appearance but, giving him a look of distinction.

Once on the shore, the soldier led the way through the rough grass, followed in turn by the priest, the official party, and a procession of sailors. Winding their way to an elevated spot sheltered by a wall of vegetation, the soldier looked at the priest as if seeking approval. The priest nodded his head, and the party formed into a circle.

The cleric's eye, long accustomed to identifying plants and trees, noted the myrtles, bays, and cedars. With easy familiarity the smaller man flipped open the prayer book and read the first lesson for the morning.

"Let us pray."

The priest dropped to his knees. The earth felt good. After fifty-seven days on a tossing ship, he welcomed the soil of the American continent. It had been a long trip, and John Wesley, the priest, knelt side by side with Oglethorpe, the governor, and offered a prayer of thanksgiving for a safe trip and for their arrival in America.

Wesley recalled his first acquaintance with Oglethorpe. His father had written letters of encouragement to this same man. Strangely enough a significant contact had come inadvertently through his father.

The older Wesley had spent a good number of his latter days writing a lengthy six-hundred-page volume on the book of Job. It meant so much to him, and although he had received permission to dedicate it to Queen Caroline, he did not live to see the finished production. Now that the book had come from the publishers Susanna Wesley asked her son John to make the trip to London to place the volume into the royal hands.

In the ceremony, John, on his knees, handed over the precious book. However, Queen Caroline had other things on her mind. Exhilarated from romping around the room with her maids of honor and anxious to get back to her fun, she gave the book a cursory glance and remarked, "It is prettily bound," and to John's dismay laid it aside without as much as opening up its covers.

As disappointing as was the royal interview, the visit to London had one compensation. John renewed his acquaintance with Dr. John Burton of Corpus Christi College, Oxford. For years he had pushed for the establishment of the new colony in America. And now Dr. Burton talked with the earnest young priest about the prospect of missionary work across the Atlantic. Although an Oxford professor who had long lived in an ivory tower, Burton made it clear to John that this was no task for people who wanted a life of ease, luxury, or levity. The trustees of the colony were interested in sending a serious-minded man who would be prepared to make sacrifices and endure suffering.

So it was that Burton introduced John to the governor of Georgia, James Edward Oglethorpe. Oglethorpe, a soldier, had lived an entirely different type of life from Wesley, but he was immediately impressed by the sober young priest and offered John the position of missionary to the infant colony.

A number of motivating factors had lead to the venture in Georgia. As a member of parliament, Oglethorpe took seriously the responsibilities of the seat he occupied in the House of

Commons. On one particular occasion he visited a friend who had been thrown into debtors' prison, and he burned with indignation at the sights that met his eyes. His considerable influence in the House of Commons led to the creation of a committee charged with the responsibility of investigating the conditions of debtors' prisons.

The publication of this committee's findings initiated a number of changes. One unforeseen result was that hundreds of penniless and homeless exprisoners wandered the streets of English cities. They needed somewhere to begin life again. A new colony would provide them with a wonderful opportunity for a fresh start.

King George II granted a charter in June of 1732 creating a strip of land between South Carolina and Florida into a British colony to be named Georgia in his honor. The territory was invested in a corporation headed by twenty-one trustees. Supporters raised thirty-six thousand pounds and the House of Commons voted an appropriation of ten thousand pounds to help the new project.

Other idealistic objectives were soon added for the new "royal province." It would establish a place of refuge for some twenty thousand persecuted Protestants who had been expelled from their homes by the Bishop of Salzburg. Moreover, the new colony would give impetus to missionary activity by providing a basis for work with the Indians.

Another practical purpose, not often mentioned, was to prevent the expansion of the Spanish northward from their base in Florida. This consideration occupied a much larger place in the minds of English colonizers than many were willing to admit.

The colony had already been in existence for a year when John Wesley met Oglethorpe. On the bluff, now the location of the city of Savannah, stood the homes of the new colonists.

Each freeholder received fifty acres of land. Five of these were close to the main township of Savannah and the other forty-five were located in a more distant part of the colony.

Oglethorpe, the soldier, believed in uniformity. Each house was identical in appearance and size, 16 feet by 24 feet, with unplaned siding, wooden floors, and shingle roofs. They stood somewhat somberly in orderly rows, lining the square blocks.

On the right flank of the settlement between the houses and the forest stood two lonely sentinels, the lookout post where the sentry kept a watchful eye towards the forest, and the parsonage house. That parsonage between the Indians, on the one hand, and those seeking a new life, on the other, symbolized the task awaiting some young priest in Georgia.

As he talked with John, Oglethorpe unrolled the map. Pointing to the parsonage location, he spoke of the task waiting for some man of God. To John it seemed like a Macedonian call. Haunted by the image of that parsonage he began to inquire among his friends as to their opinions. And he asked himself over and over what this could mean to him.

At the forefront of this serious man's mind was the primary task of saving his own soul. But there were other things he might gain. John believed in the myth of the noble savage. He thought of the Indians as unspoiled by civilization. They could come to the message of Christianity as little children, never having been corrupted by the vain speculations of so-called civilized people.

Many people had to be consulted—above all his mother. As they discussed the matter, she reminded John of his father's interest in the Georgia colony. The older Wesley had kept up a lively correspondence with Oglethorpe, advising him about the type of plantings to make in the new country and had even recommended his son-in-law John Whitelamb as a good prospect for chaplain.

Sitting and looking at John's handsome face and hearing him talk about the missionary adventure recalled the night of the fire to Susanna Wesley's mind. The burning of the Epworth parsonage had an air of intrigue about it. Mysterious events had transpired around the house. The conflagration which destroyed nearly all the rector's worldly goods may have been the work of some disgruntled parishioner. A strained relationship existed between this shepherd and certain members of his flock.

The flames had brightened the skies for miles around in a magnificent display that aroused the impoverished country dwellers from their beds and sent them scurrying down the potholed roads and winding pathways to the ancient Epworth Rectory. Their dreary lives had all too little entertainment, and they welcomed the drama of a large house afire, with the residents trying desperately to save a few belongings. The event would long be discussed during the lengthy winter evenings.

As a dramatic spectacle, the fire reached its climactic moment when the head and shoulders of a small six-year-old boy appeared at an upper window. The rest of the family were safely outside, but flames and smoke had trapped him in the old building.

After a valiant but futile effort to re-enter the house, the vicar retreated before a wall of flame. In an agony of frustration he threw himself on his knees and committed the soul of his child to God.

More practical-minded men outside the house searched in vain for a ladder, then quickly ran to the wall. While one stood with his back to the quivering structure, a comrade climbed on his shoulders and managed to reach the small boy, yanking him from his precarious perch just in the nick of time. The burning roof collapsed with a resounding crash, covering the bystanders with sparks and tinders. By a hair's breadth the small boy had been saved from a horrible death.

The drama of the occasion was not lost upon Samuel. He shouted, "Come neighbors, let us kneel down; let us give thanks to God. He has given me all my eight children; let the house go. I am rich enough."

Kneeling on the damp ground, with scantily clad family and parishioners gathered around in the eerie light from the leaping flames, the rector with a strange sense of exhilaration, despite his loss, led his flock in a fervent prayer.

His pregnant wife fought back her critical thoughts. What did he mean, "I am rich enough"? It was all right for this impractical dreamer to advertise his sentiments but already her practical woman's mind was at work trying to figure out how and where they would live.

She had had a narrow escape herself. Hampered by her advanced pregnancy she had only managed to get away from the burning house with great difficulty. Three times the flames drove her back from the hallway that led to safety. At last she made one final frantic effort and pushed her way out with scorched hands and face. Then had followed that horrible moment when it had seemed as if John would be swallowed up in the flaming inferno.

As the men carried the small boy from the burning building, Mrs. Wesley rushed over to snatch him from the rescuer's arms and hold him close to her flushed face. To her there was something symbolic about the whole episode. This boy John was her "brand from the burning."

The incident served to foster an impression Susanna had felt for some time. Nearly two years later, shortly before John's eighth birthday, Susanna in her own exquisite handwriting wrote, "I do intend to be more particularly careful of the soul of this child that thou hast so mercifully provided for, than I have been, that I may endeavor to instill into his mind the principles of true religion and virtue. Lord give me grace to do it sincerely and prudently; and bless my attempts with good success."

The word *missions* brought with it, too, the memory of the time when Samuel's duties had compelled him to be away in London for a long period of time, and he had left the curate in charge of the church services. This poor fellow, an indifferent preacher, soon wearied the spirited Susanna. Rev. Mr. Inman had one message and that was on the necessity of everyone paying his debts. No matter where he started, his sermon inevitably turned to the problem of indebtedness.

His preaching irritated Susanna. She realized it was widely known that Samuel had liabilities which kept him constantly warding off his creditors. Grimly aware that their financial problems were compounded by paying the curate's salary and there were other Christian virtues worthy of discussion, the strong-minded Susanna took the situation in hand by conducting worship in her enormous kitchen.

Her large family, a sizable congregation of itself, was soon augmented by friends. The crowds continued to grow until she had two hundred people seated on chairs, tables, floors, and peeping in through the windows.

The curate burned with indignation. He wrote a hasty letter reporting the irregular church service to the absent vicar. Samuel Wesley reacted with characteristic speed and lack of thought, ordering his wife to cease and desist from such unladylike activities and abandon her gatherings.

Susanna insisted that her husband give her a "positive command" which he could present, "before the great and awful Tribunal of our Lord Jesus Christ."

Overwhelmed with the idea of presenting a good rational argument about the inferiority of women before that tribunal Samuel had second thoughts and dropped the matter.

An unusual set of circumstances had brought the church services to birth. The rector's absence left time for reading. Her daughter Emily, while rummaging through the vicar's library, discovered a long neglected book which she carried to her mother. This story of two Danish missionaries Zeigenbalgh and Plutscho, pioneers in the East Indies, enthralled Susanna. It fanned the flames of all her latent evangelistic fervor.

Conscious of a woman's inferior station in that day, Susanna had long realized the impossibility of ever embarking upon some world-wide mission enterprise. Then came the moment of enlightenment as she realized her distinctive feminine opportunities. She had a group of bright-eyed children who looked to her for guidance and provided an obvious mission field right in her own home.

As she read the stories of her missionary heroes to the children, others came to join the group. With an ever growing congregation she moved on to the best sermons she could find. This determined woman was committed to work the spiritual revival no matter what might be the stuffy curate's opinion.

But she needed something more personal for her own children, and so she formulated a simple plan. A portion of each day was to be set apart for talking with them. She wrote a letter to her husband telling him how she put the scheme into action, "On Monday, I talk with Molly; on Tuesday with Hetty; Wednesday with Nancy; Thursday with Jacky; Friday with Patty; Saturday with Charles; and with Emily and Suky together on Sunday." In this way she launched a historic teaching ministry.

Such was the first woman to influence John Wesley. He was

her "brand from the burning," and she never let him forget it. The little boy grew of destiny into manhood with a strange sense of destiny.

From the mother who in the days of his childhood had spent so much time reading about the exploits of missionaries, came the response, "If I had twenty sons, I should rejoice if they were all so employed though I never saw them anymore."

The decision was made. John would go to Georgia.

2.

The Golden Isles

April 9, 1734

WHEN MRS. JENKINS, like many another English mother, insisted that Bobby wash his ears, she little realized that one of them would one day cause a war between two great nations. Grown to manhood, and now Captain Robert Jenkins, he sailed his brig *Rebecca* through the West Indies on a trip back to England in the year 1731. A Spanish guardship fired a shot across his bow and when he tried to ignore it, the Spaniards forcibly boarded the *Rebecca.*

After a fruitless search for contraband goods, the Spaniards strung the unfortunate Jenkins from the yardarm, hoping thereby to persuade him to reveal the hiding place of his illicit cargo. Lowered at last to the deck, the indignant Jenkins jumped to his feet warning his torturers that he sailed under His Majesty's Britannic flag, whereupon a Spanish soldier seized hold of his already partly severed ear, tore it off, and threw it at him, exclaiming, "Carry that to your king."

Which was exactly what Jenkins tried to do. Seven years later he appeared before a committee of the House of Commons and dramatically produced the ear, and recalling his reactions at the time of the incident, he said, "I commended my soul to God and my cause to my country." The story fanned the flames of patriotic pride and war was declared between England and Spain, a war which lasted until 1748 and is known as, "The War of Jenkins' Ear."

There have been many skeptical comments on the incident of Jenkins' ear, with some modern debunkers even suggesting he might never have really lost it. However, there can be no denial of the war that followed and the name by which it came to be known. Moreover, the event, apocryphal or real, typified the strained relationship between Spain and England concerning the right to sail on this portion of the high seas.

In an effort to retain her grip on the treasure of South America, Spain reluctantly allowed only one British trade vessel a year into South American waters, but resourceful British sailors soon found ways to circumvent this ban. The policing activity of Spanish ships resulted, and the British found their trade increasingly subjected to the supervision of Spain.

Today, the name Golden Isles is given a series of small islands off the Georgia coast. In the eighteenth century these islands lay in the heart of the Spanish Main. Great Spanish galleons loaded down with gold and valuable South American produce sailed up the eastern coast of America on the way to Spain. Harbors along the American coastline provided excellent bases from which British ships could sally forth to attack the treasure fleet, and to which they could flee for refuge, refitting, and resupply.

All but excluded from South America, the British majored in taking possession of the North American continent. They faced a dual threat. The French in New Orleans might at any moment sweep across country, enlist Indian allies, and attack the colonies from the rear. And Spanish adventurers seeking the mythical fountain of youth had established the first European settlement on the North American continent at St. Augustine. They also laid claim to land further north and resented the intrusion of the British.

Colonists in South Carolina living on this edge of the British Empire were starkly aware of the problem. The governor and assembly, meeting in solemn conclave on April 9th 1734, sent a grandiose memorial to King George II reminding him of the twofold threat of Spain along the coast, and of France in the interior. In its eighteenth century language this document shows the importance of a move to build a fort and settle colonists on the stretch of water in the vicinity of the Altahamah River.

In the year of 1734 Oglethorpe had sailed down the Frederica River until he came to a bluff located on a sharp U-turn on the waterway. Despite the driving rain of that January day, Oglethorpe, standing under the shelter of a great oak tree, saw possibilities of establishing a fortified settlement. On the western side of the river stretched miles of marshes which would bog down any invader. The peculiar position at that curve in the river would provide the defenders an unobstructed view of the channel, with deep water close inshore allowing boats to berth and unload supplies. This was a ready-made spot upon which to build a town.

Returning to England, Oglethorpe received a tremendous welcome. The hero of the hour, a ship was named in his honor and poems were written in praise of his achievements. The trustees of the colony accepted the recommendations he brought, decided to establish a settlement on the southern edge of the colony, and to name it Frederica as a tribute to Frederick Louis, the Prince of Wales.

The choice of names was not the best augury of success. Born in Hanover, this unfortunate man had been designated Prince of Wales in 1727. He spent most of his adult days in a bitter feud with his father. And to cap it all, it was his son who, as King George III, alienated his subjects in the American colonies and ultimately lost possession of what was to become the most prosperous nation in the world.

Happily unaware of the future blundering activity of Frederick's son, the trustees of the colony of Georgia proceeded to make careful selection of the new settlers to settle Fort Frederica.

3.

Four Beef Days

February 5, 1735

"YOUR ATTENTION PLEASE."

Benjamin Martyn's thin reedy voice, which one Herefordshire farmer said reminded him of a lamb's bleat, gained an immediate response from the large group of men and women assembled in the room.

The silence which blanketed that place made a noticeable contrast with the previous hubbub of conversation among the strangely assorted group of individuals. Will Harris leaned over to whisper in his wife's ear, "That is Benjamin Martyn, secretary of the trustees, and the man with him is the Earl of Egmont."

Martyn continued and announced with as much dignity as

his uncertain voice would allow, "His Grace the Earl of Egmont, chairman of the trustees of the colony of Georgia."

Shaking his head to make sure his full bottomed wig appeared to best advantage, the earl arose and walked to the center of the platform. Appearing before a group of tradespeople had little appeal to him. But occasions such as this provided only a means to an end. The new project would gain him more attention from the royal court.

In carefully measured tones he began to speak, "You have been invited here today so that we can acquaint you with the plans for a new settlement in the royal province of Georgia. I will now call upon the secretary to read to you the rules under which the new town will be established."

Benjamin Martyn adjusted his reading glasses, opened the large book in front of him, and began to read a long statement of what was known as the "Rules for the Year 1735."

Having learned from their experiences with the first group of settlers, who once they had arrived in the colony were full of complaints and made all sorts of demands, the trustees were determined to spell out every detail for this new group. Martyn read out the lists of clothes, goods, food, and tools that would be supplied to the settlers.

The document made it clear that the trustees were not only furnishing transportation, but on the trip over, the week was to be divided according to the main dinner course for each day. There were to be four "beef days," two "pork days," and one "fish day."

Even more important for many of these Englishmen who had longed to own a piece of land, the elaborate prospectus spelled out the exact grants of land they would receive and the conditions of possession.

Although the secretary read slowly, pausing periodically to clarify a statement, no restless movement marred the performance. For the assembled company these rules provided the framework within which they would begin a new life. It meant an unusual opportunity to try their fortune in the new world.

At the conclusion of the reading the Earl of Egmont stood to his feet again, "As chairman of the board of trustees, I must point out that you people assembled here today have been chosen from among the many applicants who wish to settle in the new town of Frederica.

"We want you to realize that although we will provide you with your passage across the Atlantic, land upon which to live, and a year's provisions, many difficulties lie ahead.

"The forests are wild, you will be without shelter until you build yourself a house, your food will consist of salt meat and water. You must be on constant guard against enemies, clear the ground, and cultivate the crops. The country is hot in the summer and cold in the winter. There is an abundance of flies and if you drink distilled liquor you stand in eminent danger of sickness."

The earl paused to gauge the effect of his warnings and then turned to a happier note, "But if you trust in God and work hard, you will be able to establish both yourselves and your families under comfortable circumstances."

Again a long pause, "Now is the time for you to decide. If you have any doubts as to whether you can go through with these difficulties, it would be foolish of you to go. You should by no means undertake this venture if you have any real uncertainties in your mind."

In the discussion which followed the Earl of Egmont and the secretary tried to answer every question. Many of the applicants who had been so excited at the opportunity began to have second thoughts. Although the resolution of some failed and they withdrew, others on the waiting list happily took their places and made preparations for the voyage.

The English volunteers were joined by eighty German Lutherans known as Salzburgers, under the leadership of Baron von Reck, and a band of Moravians led by Bishop David Nitschman. The total number of colonists came to two hundred and fifty-seven, and when the expedition had ultimately prepared for departure, it came to be known as "The Great Embarkation," because it constituted the largest group of settlers that had ever left for Georgia at any one time.

4.

In Perils in the Deep

October 14, 1735—February 16, 1736

After all the rush to pack and get their goods and books aboard the *Simmonds* and the *London Merchant,* the passengers settled down for a nearly two month wait before finally departing from Cowes. Their escort vessel, the H.M.S. *Hawk,* had to be fitted out for surveying the Georgia coastline, and they could not depart until she had received the approval of her captain. The delay provided opportunity for the passengers and crew to learn the routine of shipboard life.

Francis Moore, keeper of the stores, fretted about the delay. He could see how it hurt the morale of the people. Moreover it created havoc with his supplies. Appetites sharpened by the sea air, the people ate into his carefully planned provisions.

When he sought to buy replacement supplies at Spithead, the merchants, aware of his difficult situation, charged him outrageous prices.

John Wesley, convinced by past experiences that he needed the support of a team of like-minded people, had been busily at work recruiting fellow workers for the missionary venture.

The zealous Charles immediately volunteered to go, and upon John's recommendation his brother was appointed Secretary of Indian Affairs. Charles Delamotte, the son of a London sugar merchant, represented the laymen who were to grow increasingly significant in Wesley's ministry and offered to make the trip to Georgia at his own expense.

A young Oxford student named Westley Hall spent a great deal of his time with the Wesleys. And when he heard about the plans for Georgia, he enthusiastically decided to join the party, and on the basis of this decision to go to Georgia as a missionary, he was ordained to the Church of England ministry.

Another Church of England minister, Benjamin Ingham, looked like a worthy addition to the party to John, but he was unconvinced that he should go. Ingham finally agreed, however, that if for some reason Hall decided not to make the trip he would join the team. Noting Hall's enthusiasm, Ingham saw small possibility of sailing the Atlantic.

Then, just before the party was to board the ship Westley Hall decided that instead of a trip across the Atlantic he would get married. So Ingham became the fourth member of the team.

Ingham proved to be an asset and worked diligently recording the day-by-day events of the voyage. He also undertook the responsibility of preparing an important document to be known as The Solemn Agreement which the four missionaries ceremoniously signed on the eve of their departure. Ingham's handwriting set forth the significant covenant.

In the name of God Amen.

We whose names are underwritten being fully convinced that it is impossible to promote the work of God among the heathen without an entire union amongst ourselves, or that such an union should subsist unless each one will give up his single judgment to that of the majority, do agree by the help of God.

1. That none of us will undertake anything of importance, without first proposing it to the others.

2. That whenever our judgments on indivinations differ, any-one shall give of his single judgment or indivination to the others.

3. That in case of an equality after begging God's direction the matter shall be decided by lot.

J.W., C.W., B.J., C.I.

This agreement may be the key to an unusual and puzzling set of circumstances which arose later in John's Georgian ministry.

Determined to safeguard the health of his new settlers, Oglethorpe had laid in a stock of food that would relieve the monotony of a shipboard diet. Francis Moore, in charge of the stores, noted he had turnips, carrots, and onions to supplement the salt meat and protect against scurvy.

Conscious of their mission to establish a fort, Oglethorpe had also arranged for the men to spend a portion of the day learning to handle arms. Captain Hermsdorf, with Prussian precision, worked diligently to make soldiers out of his tradesmen. In a separate set of activities for the women, they were taught to knit stockings and caps and given time to mend and repair clothing. Also the new settlers were instructed on the nature of the country they were to settle—methods of farming, activities of the Indians.

The voyage over offered the Wesley party an opportunity to prepare for and practice their missionary work. Immediately upon boarding the ship, they instituted a rigid schedule which guaranteed against wasting any part of their day. Sharply at 4:00 A.M. they climbed from their bunks and spent the first hour of the day in private prayer. The hours from five to seven they gave to group Bible study. At seven they ate breakfast, followed at eight with public prayers conducted for the passengers. From nine till twelve each had his particular task. John studied grammar, Mr. Delamotte studied Greek, Charles prepared sermons, and Mr. Ingham studied or spent time instructing the children. Every hour was accounted for.

Some of the passengers soon began to complain about the mission ministry of John and his friends. A Mr. Johnson, the son of the late governor of South Carolina, became extremely irate and demanded action. Unfortunately, he occupied an important position in the expedition. This sister colony had already been a thorn in Oglethorpe's side, as traders from there, thinking only of profits, had sold arms to the Spaniards. Oglethorpe hoped Johnson would establish good relationships with South Carolina's leaders and bring the cooperation necessary for two colonies facing England's enemies, Spain and France.

After listening to Johnson's indignant complaints, Oglethorpe sent for John, and while acknowledging the absurdities of Johnson's demands, explained the importance of placating him.

Anxious to cooperate, Wesley hurried around seeking an alternative meeting place that would be less offensive to Mr. Johnson. They finally reached a compromise. Mr. Johnson slept late so they could have morning prayers in the cabin. Afternoon prayers would be conducted in the fore hatchway between decks—a dirty and noisy spot that would accommodate only a quarter of the congregation.

The same Mr. Johnson chafed at the delay in departure and after a month of waiting, first for the escort vessel and then for a fair wind, he gathered all his goods together and left the ship to return to London.

Then there was Mr. Horton. He had been the undersheriff of Herefordshire and had accumulated a sizeable amount of capital. On the basis of his reputation and the fact that he would take ten servants, Horton had received a grant of land from the trustees. In an immoderate celebration of his departure he spent most of the waiting time on a drunken spree and disappeared to his cabin for prolonged sessions "sleeping it off."

With their master drunk the greatest part of the time the servants were free to do as they wished. Anne Seabury, Horton's maid, caused so many problems that Oglethorpe finally ordered her put ashore.

Horton believed that the Wesleys were behind all of this and decided to take revenge. Knowing they retired early, he waited until midnight, then climbed to the deck that formed the roof of their cabin and launched into a heavy-footed dance which soon had them all awake.

This was the beginning of a strained relationship which constantly bothered John all the days of his Frederica ministry in America. In time Horton gave up his intemperate ways but not his antagonism to Wesley. As he advanced in influence in the colony, he used his new status to make life increasingly difficult.

Fortunately some passengers were eager for spiritual ministrations. None more so than a little group of women. They were all married—Mrs. Lawley, Mrs. Welch, Mrs. Moore, and particularly Mrs. Hawkins.

Mrs. Hawkins and John met shortly after he boarded the *Simmonds*. Wesley, with an evident note of disapproval, described her as "a gay young woman." She attended church, and a sermon in which he had spoken on the nature of Christ evoked an obvious response. Later they sat together in a convenient spot in the cabin, and she listened with rapt attention as John discussed religion.

On one occasion a religious discussion with John so overwhelmed Mrs. Hawkins that the tears flowed down her cheeks as she said, "My mother died when I was ten years old. Some of her last words were, 'Child, fear God, and though you lose me, you shall never want a friend.' "

Mrs. Hawkins paused, and looking into the young cleric's eyes, she continued, "I have now found a friend when I most wanted and least expected one."

John anticipated that Dr. and Mrs. Hawkins could well be the most influential people in the colony. If he could gain their friendship and lead them into a deep religious commitment, they would be of tremendous value to his work. Through them he could influence so many other people. John came to believe that Mrs. Hawkins' responsive spirit might make her the key to the situation. She in turn could work on Dr. Hawkins. It seemed an admirable strategy.

While Beata Hawkins had the outstanding personality, Anne Welch, pretty, vain, and friendly, took the prize for physical beauty and an elaborate wardrobe of clothes. Twenty-six years old, she had two children, James and John. She was pregnant again and resented the inconvenience of her condition and the temporary deprivation of not wearing her pretty clothes.

But she was astute enough to turn her liability into an asset. For many years of his life John had watched the annual pregnancies of his mother, and he felt a deep concern for Mrs. Welch's condition. Governor Oglethorpe, who had an eye for a pretty girl, admired the courage of this young woman and was very solicitous for her welfare—too solicitous some passengers thought.

The journey on the cramped ship tested the endurance of Mrs. Welch who periodically fainted—particularly when either the governor or the young priest happened to be around.

On Thursday, 18th of December as John and Oglethorpe took a turn around the deck they heard the sound of a coughing spasm coming from Mrs. Welch's cramped quarters. Oglethorpe ordered the sick woman moved into his cabin. He had his servant swing a hammock for him in a convenient spot, leaving Anne Welch to enjoy the comforts of the best accommodations on the ship.

The display of attention heightened Mrs. Welch's conviction that she had not long for this life. She sent John a message that she knew she was dying and requested that he give her Holy Communion so she might be the better prepared for entrance to heaven.

John hurried to the cabin and solemnly conducted the service. Shortly after receiving the bread and wine, Mrs. Welch began to feel better, and John marvelled at the power of heavenly grace.

Faced with so many calls on his time, John tried to minister with impartiality. Mrs. Moore, Oglethorpe's servant, was as fat, motherly, and plain as Mrs. Welch was youthful and attractive. She suddenly took to her bed. Though the surgeon hurried to help, she let him know she needed spiritual rather than physical ministrations. John came running and the attention-starved woman recounted a story of her failures and misdeeds. She had noticed that Mr. Wesley had visited the other sick women and read to them. Would he please read to her?

Of course he would. John made it a point to sit with her each day and read from Norris' *Christian Prudence*. Mrs. Moore soon tired of this heavy material and within two days claimed she was so much improved that she no longer needed John to call on her.

The seaman who stood at the cabin door found it difficult to keep a straight face as he reported to John that Mrs. Lawley lay ill in her cabin and requested that Mr. Wesley call on her. Arriving at the cabin, he discovered the sick woman wanted to take Holy Communion, but he felt she should be instructed before being admitted to the sacrament. So he made arrangements to come each day and read Law's *Christian Perfection.*

One morning Mrs. Hawkins happened by the Lawley cabin during the reading. She quietly took a stool and listened. But it wasn't long before she too came down with a mysterious illness that put her to bed. John called on her and found that she profited from his ministry. As she sat propped up in bed, he spent a great deal of time reading to her from *Christian Prudence.* Beata smiled in appreciation for all he was doing, but inwardly speculated about the inordinately large supply of prudence with which John was equipped.

But she played the role of the spiritually penitent to the hilt and frequently wept over her sins and wicked ways and confessed her past failures to the priest. John, tremendously impressed, invited his brother Charles to come to the cabin and witness this miracle of grace.

For once Charles showed more perception than John. Mrs. Hawkins did not impress him. As soon as they could get away from the cabin, he led John off to a secluded spot on the deck and told him that in his opinion Beata Hawkins was a phony. Her display of religious concern was nothing more than an ill-disguised attempt to ingratiate herself with John. But John could not—or would not—understand his brother's skeptical attitude.

It might have been anticipated that there would be trouble with four women living in close shipboard quarters. Competition for the spiritual ministrations of a Church of England priest aggravated the situation. The inevitable happened, and the women fell to quarreling among themselves.

Just about the time John felt he had effected a reconciliation of sorts among them he discovered that their husbands had entered the fray. In their frustration they turned on John.

After one stormy encounter the men decided to quit attendance at prayers. Moreover, they prevailed on a number of other passengers to join their boycott.

Cooped up in cramped quarters, living on a monotonous diet, beset by petty jealousies, with four members of the Holy Club seeking to deepen the colonists' religious life and contrary winds slowing down their speed, it was small wonder tempers were frayed and irritation levels lowered among the passengers. Even such a matter as the distribution of water became a big issue and Oglethorpe had to appoint new officers to take over the responsibility. Passengers aggravated by the Wesleys felt they were behind it all. And as if to compound the misery, three successive storms came with mounting fury.

It was Saturday, January 17—over three months since they had boarded the ship and still there was no sight of land. A westerly blow kept the clumsy craft tacking across wind, sailing miles but making no progress towards America.

The ship's passengers reminded John of the children of Israel headed for the promised land. And like those ungrateful pilgrims, the settlers "murmured." Nothing pleased them.

The succeeding six days brought leaden skies and gradually subsiding seas, but the following Friday evening the fury of the storm burst upon them. The weary captain gave up all hope of battling the sea and let the ship drive before the raging winds.

Storms always brought testing to John who believed a good Christian should be ready for death at any moment. Sensing his inner concern and fear, he asked himself, "How is it that you have no faith?"

As if to confirm his fear, the sea swelled and inundated the ship, hurling him down on the deck. Dazed, he climbed to his feet, certain for a moment that it must be resurrection day in which the sea was giving up its dead.

Sunday the 25th brought the worst of all. The roaring winds created strange moaning, whining noises that reminded John of human cries of distress, while the enormous waves tossed the craft like a matchbox. And every ten minutes, methodical John carefully timed and noted it, there came a terrifying shock as if the bow of the ship had rammed an unyielding rock.

At the height of the storm a deeply agitated young couple and their child demanded to see John. It seems that the child had been privately christened, but in this moment of fear they wanted it rechristened by an official priest of the church just in case they did not come through the storm. John obliged and wondered.

Later, Wesley struggled on down the passageway, holding to the walls in an effort to keep his feet, and finally reached the cabin where the Germans were meeting. He wrote down his experience:

> "In the midst of the psalm wherewith their service began (wherein we were mentioning the power of God), the sea broke over, split the mainsail in pieces, covered the ship, and poured in between the decks, as if the great deep had already swallowed us up. A terrible screaming began among the English. The Germans looked up, and without intermission calmly sang on.
>
> "I asked one of them afterwards, 'Were you not afraid?'
>
> "He answered, 'I thank God, no.'
>
> "I asked, 'But were not your women and children afraid?'
>
> "He replied mildly, 'No, our women and children are not afraid to die.'
>
> "From them I went to their crying trembling neighbours, and found myself enabled to speak with them in boldness and to point out to them the difference in the hour of trial between him that feareth God and him that feareth Him not. At twelve the wind fell. This was the most glorious day which I have hitherto seen."

The sight of the emerging shoreline of America brought a sense of relief to John. The journey had been arduous and trying. Nearly four months cooped up in this small ship were enough for most of the people on board. For many of the passengers the outstanding memory would be of a group of quarreling women and with a priest fussing around trying to keep the peace.

5.

A Bower of Palmetto Leaves

February 16, 1736–1742

IT MIGHT BE IMAGINED that Oglethorpe's arrival at Cockspur Island off the Georgian coast after the long trip would bring a solution to his many problems. Unfortunately this was not so, and the governor found himself confronted with a series of crises that might have driven a lesser man to distraction.

Before leaving Georgia on his last trip to England, Oglethorpe made plans to build a lighthouse on Cockspur Island and had the materials prepared in Savannah. He had engaged Wallace Blytheman, whose reputation was that of a skillful workman, to transport the materials to Cockspur and erect the structure. Ten men had been hired to help Blytheman, and the governor had made it clear that he expected the building to be completed by the time of his return.

Now, as the *Simmonds* dropped anchor off the Georgian coast, Oglethorpe looked in vain for his lighthouse. Hurrying ashore he followed the pathway through the brush and arriving at the previously chosen spot, stood rooted to the ground, overwhelmed at the sight that met his eyes.

The area had been cleared of trees and brush timber, and bricks lay scattered around. A foundation barely twenty-four inches high marked out the base of a projected structure, but that was all. On the further side of the clearing a group of men were sitting lazily on the ground. As Oglethorpe approached, one of the men got up and walked towards them.

The unfortunate Blytheman stood as if at the last Judgment Day as Oglethorpe demanded to know why, after all this time and expense, the lighthouse was barely started. After the first shock Blytheman recovered his composure and launched into a long and improbable explanation. The chosen spot had been covered with large trees that not only had to be felled but the roots removed. Transportation of materials from Savannah took much longer than had been anticipated, special braces had to be built because of the type of construction, and the foundation proved to be very difficult.

The irate Oglethorpe, in no mood for letting Blytheman off the hook, pressed him for the real reason. By clever and detailed questioning he finally broke the tradesman down, and he admitted his ten men had just wasted their time. It seems that traders from Carolina had come with rum for sale. And no sooner were the men paid than they would go on a drinking spree.

Frustrated and annoyed the governor rebuked Blytheman and then took Wesley and several leaders of the expedition to one side to discuss the situation. His present inclination was to prosecute Blytheman and have him thrown into jail. But what would happen to the lighthouse? There were so few craftsmen available that it might never get built.

Oglethorpe finally decided to give Blytheman another chance, and appointed Mr. Vanderplank as superintendent of the project. Under a new agreement the men would be paid as the work was completed, and the governor warned Blytheman that he would certainly take him into court if his work were in any way unsatisfactory.

Solution of this problem only prepared the way for another with the Salzburgers and the Moravians in the party. The Lutherans had decided they would prefer to join their fellow religionists at Ebeneezer. Similarly, the pacifist Moravians were unenthusiastic about manning a fort at Frederica and preferred to make their home with their brethren at Irene. Oglethorpe used all his persuasive powers to change their minds. He told them there was small possibility of war, and when they asked about muskets, cannon, and other weapons, he quoted the old English proverb, "Caution is the mother of safety."

Seeing they were obdurate, Oglethorpe finally accepted the inevitable, and although it meant the loss of half his settlers, he acceded to their request.

The one bright spot in it all was when Captain Hermsdorf announced he did not intend to go with his countrymen. In front of them all he stood up and declared that, though a German, he had understood the purpose of the embarkation and would serve with Governor Oglethorpe.

His biggest problem lay with the captains of the *Simmonds* and *London Merchant* who had originally agreed to land the settlers and their stores at the sight of Fort Frederica. But the waterway to Frederica was uncharted, and with no pilot available, they were unwilling to risk their ships. Oglethorpe hurried to Savannah where he had to purchase the cargo of the sloop *Midnight* with the stipulation that the goods be delivered at Frederica. Captains Thomas and Cornish of the *Simmonds* and the *London Merchant* boarded the *Midnight* to make the trip so that they could learn the channel, and thus be able to return and sail their ships to Frederica.

William Horton and Tanner with thirty single men, together with cannon, ammunition, and tools for entrenching transhipped to the *Midnight,* which left on the morning of February 16th for Frederica.

While in Savannah the busy governor procured a scout boat in which to make the trip to the new fort. It was a strongly built, swift craft with three swivel guns and places for ten oars. The crew that manned the boat for its trip to the island impressed Francis Moore who carefully recorded his reactions, paying a tribute to both the crew and the abundant coastal areas: "The crew is composed of men bred in America, bold and hardy, who lie out in the woods and upon the water months together, without a house or covering. Most of them are good hunters or fishers. By killing deer and other game they can subsist themselves in case their provisions should fail; but indeed on these sea-islands, no one can starve, since if at the worst a man was lost, there are oysters and shell-fish enough to subsist him."

On the evening of the 16th Oglethorpe, Captain Ferguson, Captain Hermsdorf, Ingham, and three Indians joined the crew and set out on the scout boat to try to catch the *Midnight* before she arrived at the fort. The governor's enthusiasm had affected the men who rowed vigorously while Oglethorpe urged them on. The usually stolid Indians caught the spirit and insisted on taking a turn at the oars, demonstrating their unusual rowing ability. They had developed the Yamassee stroke in which they took a long and short stroke alternately and propelled the boat at a good speed.

Wednesday, February 18th, the scout boat reached St. Simons Island, and a few hours later the sloop *Midnight* sailed into sight. All hands worked at unloading the boats and the governor traced the outline of a storehouse. The men dug out the soil to a depth of three feet using it to build a bank around the new building. They cut stripling oak trees for ridgepoles and supports, and a thatching of palmetto leaves covered the whole. Starting early in the day they worked on until sunset when they wearily carried the stores under the protecting roof of the new shelter.

Friendly Indians had gathered to watch the peculiar ways of the white men and that evening brought gifts of game. The men built a great fire, roasted the animals, and ate heartily. Tired from the journey and with full stomachs they were soon asleep, with the exception of the not-so-alert sentries.

First thing the next morning Oglethorpe was at work. He, ". . . traced out a Fort . . . by cutting up the Turf from the ground, dug enough of the Ditch and raised enough of the Rampart for a Sample for the men to work upon." The whole enterprise bore the marks of careful planning. Oglethorpe brought with him detailed drawings of the fort layout. As this installation was the heart of a system of defenses, it had to be done right. Many hours had been spent with the Swiss engineer Samuel Augspourer who planned and supervised the construction and helped train the settlers in the tactics of defense.

Leaving his first group of settlers at work, Oglethorpe made the journey back to the waiting ships in the Savannah River. His arrival at Cockspur Island brought a confrontation with yet another crisis. The captains of the *Simmonds* and the *London Merchant* still refused to risk taking their vessels down the waterway to Frederica. Oglethorpe realized he would have to transport everything to Frederica by open boat—a six-day journey. So he offered the settlers the option of remaining at Savannah, but they agreed to continue on to Frederica.

Supplies not likely to be harmed by the weather were stowed on nearby Tybee Island, and the settlers boarded open boats for the trip. With justifiable sense of pride Oglethorpe was able to write to the trustees, "I have at last got all ye people to St. Simons." He had 116 people, which was less than half the number that originally constituted the "Great Embarkation."

The sight of St. Simons Island gladdened the eyes of the weary voyagers as the main party of settlers concluded their journey with the landing at Frederica. Set off by the low flat uniform marshes on the west, magnificent oaks towered above a profusion of lush growth. As if some deity had decorated for their coming, Spanish moss festooned the massive trees scattered across the 35-acre area, while thick growth surrounding the old Indian gardens promised protection from an enemy and rich land for cultivation.

The mixture of objectives behind the whole Georgian settlement were no more clearly indicated than in the manner of selecting the immigrants. The early waves of settlers, a mixed bag, came in part from England's debtors' prisons. In addition there was a liberal sprinkling of continental refugees from religious persecution. By way of contrast, the settlers at Frederica were carefully selected, hand-picked for a special purpose.

These first forty families, consisting of forty-four men and seventy-two women and children, brought with them a variety of skills. Their trades and professions included hatter, tailor, dyer, weaver, tanner, shoemaker, lawyer, carpenter, bricklayer, surveyor, accountant, baker, tallow candler, cooper blacksmith, wheelwright, surgeon, and midwife. This diversity of skills augered well for a lonely outpost which would have to be self-sufficient for long periods of time.

The spiritual welfare of the settlement was under the care of Rev. Charles Wesley. John had remained in Savannah while Charles traveled with this main body of settlers and eagerly entered upon what was to be a brief but memorable ministry. On the first Sunday his congregation numbered twenty including Governor Oglethorpe. They gathered under a massive oak tree, now known as the Wesley Oak and still standing on St. Simons Island this very day.

The fortifications were the first concern and to these the workmen gave their immediate attention. Work progressed rapidly, and the major part of the initial phase was completed within a month. One of the settlers described it, ". . . a battery of cannon mounted which commanded the river, and the part almost built, the rampart raised with green sod." The fort stood ready to operate in its role as defender of the colony.

Samuel Augspourer, the surveyor, also worked diligently at planning the town, situated east of the fort. Streets were laid out and planted with orange trees. Located at the most southern point of all the British settlements on the American mainland this town, except for the width of its streets, was a typical English village. Broad Street, seventy-five feet wide, ran right through the center of the town, crossed by Barracks Street and dividing buildings into two wards, North Ward, and South Ward. Eighty-four lots, each 60 x 90 feet, provided space for the temporary houses and the more permanent buildings of wood and tabby which would follow later. The outskirts of the town would shortly sprout with a patchwork of the colonists' vegetable gardens.

Francis Moore, who arrived just one month after the first wave of settlers, wrote a letter in which he described Frederica as he saw it, "Each family had a bower of palmetto leaves, finished upon the back street in their own lands; the side towards the front street was set out for their houses. These palmetto bowers were very convenient shelters, being tight in the hardest rains; they were about twenty foot long and fourteen foot wide, and in regular rows, looked handsome, and of a good color. The whole appeared something like a camp; for the bowers looked like tents, only being larger and covered with palmetto leaves instead of canvas." Obviously the tradesmen were applying their talents with good effect.

On the parade ground near the river they pitched three tents, two for Governor Oglethorpe and one for Mr. Horton.

Frederica became a boomtown and continued on in an impetus which lasted just twelve years. In this period the skilled workmen labored at constructing the most expensive English fort on the American continent. It became the center of a system of fortifications which included Fort St. George on St. George Island, St. Andrews on Cumberland Island, another at St. Simons Island, and a fort at Darien.

A surge of life came with Oglethorpe's Regiment (42nd Foot). These six hundred and fifty men arrived in 1738 and went to work building the second fort on the southern end of St. Simons Island. Frederica entered its heyday. Conscious of his new strength, Oglethorpe reacted to the Spanish killing of two highland soldiers by invading Florida. After considerable success, including the capture of the fortress of Castillo de San Marcos, he retreated before the oncoming stormy season.

Reprisals came in 1742 when the Spanish force of fifty-one ships and three thousand men invaded Georgia. The orders were to seize the fortified island of St. Simons and then, "proceed northward devastating, laying waste, sacking and burning." News of the approach caused consternation among the thousand defenders under Oglethorpe's command. After a brief conflict at Fort St. Simons, British forces spiked their guns and beat a strategic retreat, allowing the Spaniards to occupy the fort and control the southern portion of the island.

On July 7th the Spanish troops advanced along the roadway to a position within a mile of Fort Frederica and set the stage for the Battle of Bloody Marsh. In a desperate move, Oglethorpe left a skeleton crew of men to guard the fort against attack by water and stationed the rest of his troops near the center of the island at a bend between the marsh and the dense woods. When the numerically superior force of Spanish troops appeared, Oglethorpe's men retreated, leaving a detachment of Scotsmen and Indians concealed among the trees.

Confident of victory, the Spaniards stacked their arms and prepared a meal. A Scottish bonnet cautiously raised on a pike above the thick undergrowth gave the signal for an attack which completely routed the Spanish forces.

The tide had turned and the Spanish threat to Georgia gradually disappeared. With victory came loss for the barracks town of Fort Frederica, for without the money brought by the soldiers it withered and died. Across the years local inhabitants cannibalized the houses, sawed up the tabby, and carried it off, leaving the once proud town of Frederica as crumbling ruins on a neglected field.

6.

The Poor Heathens

February 19–April 4, 1736

JOHN ONLY HAD EYES for the noble red men of America. He had come to preach to them and he must make as many contacts as possible. He now felt the time had come for him to return the call they had made earlier and visit their village.

Thursday, February 19th, he rose at 3:30 in the morning and boarded a boat to make the trip to call on what he describes as, "The poor heathens." The forces of nature battled against them. They rowed against a stiff wind and did not arrive in Savannah until 10:30 A.M.

John had heard that the Indians were living some four miles northwest of Savannah so he looked for a guide. When at last one had been found, they set out on their way. A three-hour trek through the forest brought them at last to Cowpen, and he headed immediately for the house of Mrs. Musgrove. To John, this Indian married to an Englishman seemed to symbolize the union of Indian and white. She lived in a crude house, and John's orderly spirit cringed before the disorder, untidiness, and the smell. However, she was more than willing to help him contact the Indians, and the whole party moved down to the village. Disappointment welled up within John when they discovered the chief was away on a hunting trip.

Returning to Savannah, John decided to make the most of his visit and went to the colony supply center presided over by Mr. Causton, who also occupied the position of chief magistrate. The magistrate smiled graciously and invited him to be seated.

"Governor Oglethorpe has told me of you and his high estimate of your work. I am pleased at the prospect of us having such a learned and pious priest to minister amongst us."

Having paid his tribute to John's office, the magistrate launched himself into a long speech about the virtues of the colony's judicial system. He finally concluded by metaphorically doffing his hat to the priest. "And you know, Mr. Wesley, I believe in the power of true religion. That's where you come in. You are one of the most important persons in this colony. We are going to do everything we can to help you with your work."

When at last John left Causton's supply house, he had a sense of well-being. With Savannah in the hands of a man like Mr. Causton, anxious to encourage religion, he would have an excellent field for his work.

If John had lived in a later day, he would have heard people like Causton described with the word sociopath. Personable, plausible, and attractive, they are clever manipulators. The rules of society have never been internalized. They know the skills of relationship with their fellows; it may be they have learned them too well, and use this knowledge to maneuver fellow humans for their own purposes.

But John, like so many from the governor on down accepted Causton at face value. This man had come with the first company of immigrants in 1733, and being on the ground floor, had made the most of his opportunity. In some remarkable manner he covered up his past English record of fraud with public revenue. As one writer sees it, he was, "Naturally proud, covetous, cunning, and deceitful." With Oglethorpe so often away from Savannah, Causton became the dictator of the infant colony, presiding over the distribution of the stores provided by the trustees for the colonists. Instead of doing this impartially, he used his power to reward his friends and punish his opponents.

Causton, in the course of his brushes with the law, had become a jailhouse lawyer. And in his new position he set himself up as chief magistrate, assisted by other cipher magistrates. His impressive bodyguard consisted of eight freeholders armed with guns and bayonets. A travesty of the British judicial system, he conducted the court in shocking manner, intimidating juries, dispensing summary justice, and threatening punishment at the stocks, whipping post, or loghouse prison. When the trustees sent out a Mr. Gordon in 1732 to act as magistrate, Causton in his position of keeper of the stores refused him provisions and finally forced him out of the colony.

Later on a grand jury that he had manipulated to accuse John Wesley could finally stand him no longer and found him guilty of abusing his powers as keeper of the public stores. In October of 1738 the trustees turned Causton out of office. The stores were sold to pay the deficit in the operation, and Causton was required to leave Savannah.

But at this moment he was riding high. He held the most

important legal position in Savannah, presided over the government stores, and was living well, with a town house in addition to a country plantation. He liked the look of John. The serious young priest would bring the respectability of religion to the new and growing settlement in which there were already problems of law and order.

That night the Caustons sat and talked about the new priest. Mrs. Causton had seen John and heard about his good looks and dedication to his work. Impressed, she babbled on. Just a bit too serious to be sure, but once he faced the realities of life in Savannah he would probably loosen up.

Mr. Causton found himself in one of his rare moments of agreement with his wife. "I think he is just what we need. Unfortunately, he has already antagonized many of the colonists who came over on the *Simmonds*. But Oglethorpe really thinks highly of him. It won't hurt us to cultivate him."

"And he is unmarried," chimed in Mrs. Causton. "What a wonderful husband he would make for Sophia."

"It would certainly help with the Mellichamp situation," responded the chief magistrate.

Sophia Hopkey, their niece, was presently the biggest thorn in the Causton side. Mrs. Causton's pretty eighteen-year-old niece had come to live with them. The girl had money in her own right and at first the Caustons gave her a royal welcome. But the responsibilities of looking after a wealthy teenager had grown irksome. Particularly when Tom Mellichamp began to court her. This young man had already been involved in a number of brushes with the law and the Caustons were doing everything they could to break up the relationship.

In the meantime, John's biggest problem was finding somewhere to live in Savannah. In the early days he took up residence with the Moravian Christians. Watching their activities and living with them confirmed his previous high estimate of their religious life.

John preached his first sermon in Savannah on "Love." The reading from the Epistle was 1 Corinthians 13. With clarity and insight he preached about agape love—a love that gives. He little knew it, but a far more earthly love was about to give him trouble in his American ministry.

The following Saturday, March 13th, John received an invitation from the Caustons to come by their house to meet some friends. He arrived at 9:00 A.M. and Mr. Causton introduced him to his niece Sophia and her friend Miss Fosset. Nodding politely to them, John gravitated quite naturally to Van Reck, one of the Moravians. These German Christians continued to fascinate him, and John had many questions to ask. It soon became obvious to Miss Hopkey and Miss Fosset that while the priest was greatly taken up with Van Reck and the story of his continental experiences he had little interest in the women.

They met again ten days later. On Tuesday, November 23rd, John went to conduct the service for evening prayer and found only two people in his congregation, Miss Hopkey and Miss Fosset. Six o'clock in the evening was probably an awkward time; nevertheless, he would have normally been distressed at such a small attendance, but this evening things looked different. The devout posture of the young ladies and the attentive way they listened encouraged him.

At the conclusion of the service the women lingered to talk with John. The lonely bachelor responded to them. He was going back to the rectory. Would they care to visit for a while? They shyly accepted the invitation and the three of them spent an interesting evening talking together. They discussed the most solemn subjects as John tried to probe the depth of their religious experience and help them "become open." After they left he noted in his Journal with a sense of satisfaction that they were "very serious," and "seriously affected."

A week later Ingham landed from the Frederica boat bearing

a disquieting letter from his brother Charles. Charles was destined to become the song writer of Methodism with thousands of hymns to his credit, but the same emotionality that gave his songs such a mass appeal sometimes confused his judgment.

At Frederica Charles had enthusiastically entered upon his ministry and set about to make Fort Frederica into a city of God. In the process he alienated people from him and created antagonisms with settlers from the governor down.

As he stumbled in and out of situations, he let two women lead him into the worst imbroglio of all. Mrs. Hawkins had developed an implacable hostility to Charles on the voyage across the Atlantic, and he should have been on the alert when she and Mrs. Welch invited him to the Welch residence. He listened in amazement as they poured out a story of unfaithfulness to their respective husbands.

Then the bombshell. The same man had seduced both of them—Oglethorpe, the governor.

Charles was overwhelmed by the news but not as upset as he would have been if he could have seen what happened following his departure.

Mrs. Welch and Mrs. Hawkins had hurried down to call on the governor. In much the same chastened manner used with Charles, they now told their story to the governor but with a different twist. As they related it now, Charles Wesley, Oglethorpe's secretary, was at this moment spreading the story around the colony that Oglethorpe had an adulterous relationship with both of them.

That news infuriated Oglethorpe. While he had great respect for John Wesley, he had come to dislike the self-righteous Charles. This conceited clergyman was supposed to be his secretary, but while secretarial work lay neglected, he had been pestering everybody with his impractical ideas. And now to spread a malicious story about him—this was the last straw.

A fighter of no mean order, Oglethorpe had battled in the House of Commons for the poor in debtors' prisons, led the formation and founding of this colony, and stood ready in this outpost to fight the might of Spain. Would he let a parson stand in his way? He resolved to launch upon a campaign to take the conceited priest down a peg.

Charles had also caused a strict Sabbath observance law to be promulgated, and when Dr. Hawkins fired off a musket on Sunday he had been arrested. The whole outpost was in an uproar, and the majority of the settlers were hostile to Charles whom they saw as a meddlesome nuisance. Oglethorpe continued his campaign even to the point of having a servant confiscate Charles' bed. The climax came when an irate settler made an attempt on his life.

As John read the leter in which Charles gave the summary of these events, it seemed to him that a band of demons had taken over the Frederica colony. Recalling the biblical statement, he reminded himself that devils such as these came not out except by prayer and fasting. He and Ingham prayed and agreed they would not eat meat or drink wine. They limited themselves to living on bread in a self-sacrificing effort to do battle with the entrenched forces of wickedness at work in Frederica.

John knew he must go immediately to help Charles, so he hastened to complete arrangements to leave on the first available boat which happened to be a periagua. Francis Moore described the unusual craft, "These periaguas are long flat bottomed boats, carrying from twenty to thirty-five tons. They have a kind of a forecastle and a cabin; but the rest is open. They have two masts which they can strike and sails like schooners. They generally row with two oars."

The awkward boat needed a northerly wind to set sail for Frederica from Savannah. As if the powers of wickedness in high places were united in an effort to stop his departure, a howling gale blew in the wrong direction. The boatman looked at the lowering sky and dismally shook his head. There was no possibility of getting under way while these conditions prevailed.

Mr. Causton came by to visit John. His mind was full of Tom Mellichamp. The violent young man had been in trouble again, and when he was arrested, he sent for Miss Sophia. She would have gone had her aunt not forbidden it. Causton saw himself caught in a cleft stick. His duty demanded he deal firmly with Mellichamp, but there were people who claimed his attitude came from resentment because Mellichamp had courted Miss Sophia.

No sooner had Causton departed than Tom Mellichamp's mother knocked at John's door. His heart went out to her. He had watched his own mother when she worried over her children. At his best, the tender hearted young priest reassured the distraught woman that he would visit her son at the first opportunity.

It upset John that all these things had thrown his plans out of gear. Morning prayer had to be postponed until 10 o'clock. The faithful Miss Sophia and Miss Fosset sat in his congregation, and after the benediction, they remained behind for a visit.

Three days passed before the boat finally got under way. Each morning he climbed down the steps to the landing only to be told by the boatman that the prevailing winds would not let them depart. Perhaps tomorrow.

7.

Man Overboard

April 4–17, 1736

AT LONG LAST they were under way. After all the delay, at four o'clock on Sunday afternoon the clumsy periagua crawled ungracefully down the river. It inched along at funeral pace, making such slow progress that darkness caught them at Skidoway Island where they anchored for the evening.

The deck of the boat offered the only place for John to sleep. He wound the ample cloak around his slender body in a futile effort to gain refuge from the clouds of sand flies that made the traveler's life a misery. But the sleeping habits of the years took over and lulled him into a repose that neither sand flies nor talking crew nor pitching boat could disturb.

How it happened he never knew. Perhaps a large wave

rocked the ungainly vessel, but in a moment he found himself floundering in the water. A typical entry in his Journal read, "I swam around to the other side of the periagua where a boat was tied, and climbed up by the rope without any hurt other than wetting my clothes." To him the 2:00 A.M. swim in the inky blackness was just another event in a full life.

The trip needed a moment of excitement. With contrary winds they struggled on, but the industrious John, as if in an effort to counterbalance the boat's lethargy, labored in reading his Greek New Testament, the Psalms, the prayer book, and his Bible. Tormented by flies by day and sand flies by night, he nevertheless found time to pray. Not for Charles. Charles might have passed on by now. His concern was for the two who had brought his brother to this fate: Oglethorpe and Mrs. Hawkins.

Frederica at last. Oglethorpe came out in a boat to greet a surprised John and gave him a warm welcome. At the landing, amid the little knot of settlers, stood Beata Hawkins, a strange tantalizing smile on her face. John greeted her politely before hurrying on to the wretched Reed hut where Charles lay stretched on the floor. The sight of John provided strong medicine for Charles. He immediately took a turn for the better and from that moment began to show a steady improvement.

Both John and Charles were anxious to discuss the events of Frederica but feared the ears of informers. The circumstances tested their ingenuity. Trying to give the appearance of taking an afternoon stroll, they wandered down the street and headed towards the garden plots. Just as soon as they were safely out of sight, they doubled back across the thickly wooded area and hid among the trees. Even in the forest there might be enemy ears, so as much as possible they talked in Greek.

Under the grip of deep emotion Charles poured out his story, lapsing into Greek whenever he reached a specially significant point in the narration. John, one ear cocked towards the forest, found his powers of comprehension tested as he toiled to understand the statements of his distressed brother. In true Wesley fashion Charles also wrote out the account of the whole event, with appropriate Greek usage to nullify all possibilities of detection.

John found himself caught in a three-way tug. He and Charles were always close and consulted with each other about every move they planned. But their temperaments differed and they were often far apart in their thinking. Although intensely loyal to each other, they were also aware of brotherly failure. John had some questions about Oglethorpe, but the governor had always been friendly and open. Beata Hawkins was the greatest mystery of them all. How he longed for her to discover the realities of a deep religious experience.

What *could* he believe? He found himself caught in a whirl of investigations as he talked with the governor, who told him how he saw the series of events. Then Mrs. Welch told her story and there was a joint conference with Oglethorpe and Mrs. Hawkins. John Wesley repeatedly asked himself just what was the truth. Especially when Beata Hawkins remained behind after church service to plead her cause with John.

A confused John wrote up the account of his meeting with Mrs. Hawkins. It is a tribute to her persuasiveness that when John showed the statement to Charles, his brother wrote, "By a relation my brother gave me of the late experience he had with her, I was, in spite of all I had seen and heard, half persuaded into a good opinion of Mrs. Hawkins." When the victim of Beata's scheming could begin to doubt his own experiences, it says much for her sagacity.

Another problem confronted John. Oglethorpe's servants had refused Charles' request for a kettle and a bed and he became resigned to his fate and never asked for another thing from the authorities. With the depletion of his food supply,

Charles went on a hunger strike. He was making the point that if they would not give him supplies, he had no intention of begging.

Charles had a stubborn streak and John found his persuasive powers tested as he tried to talk his brother out of his determination to starve rather than ask. Finally Charles walked to the governor's tent.

As he entered, Oglethorpe greeted him, "Pray sir, sit down. I have somewhat to say to you. I hear you have spread several reports about." The confrontation proved to be so dramatic that when Charles wrote it up in his journal, he used a shorthand that no one else would be able to understand. However, they ultimately reached agreement, and Oglethorpe readily granted his request for food.

Struggling to sort out the confusion, John concluded that Mrs. Welch must be the schemer. Perhaps Mrs. Hawkins had been an innocent victim of circumstances. Governor Oglethorpe, too, seemed innocent.

The conclusion about Beata Hawkins' innocence made him feel better, but an air of mystery pervaded the whole proceedings. Some demoniac powers were making this lonely little outpost of civilization into a veritable inferno of hate, distrust, and moral confusion. He knew he must get back to Savannah, but what would happen to Charles in his absence? In his diary he wrote one descriptive word, "afraid."

He tried to get away at daybreak but had to wait for letters the governor wanted him to deliver in Savannah. Finally at 10:30 Sunday morning the boat pushed off, only to encounter a heavy rainstorm. The journey matched Frederica's chaos and turmoil. Rain, adverse winds, and no adequate shelter made the return trip unpleasant and difficult.

Why should John have hurried back to Savannah? Charles had needed him desperately, and the situation in Frederica remained critical. There was nothing really urgent about his Savannah commitments, but John felt he must get back there again. As he stood up to conduct the evening prayers and saw the white clad figure of Sophia Hopkey sitting in the congregation, there swept over him a guilty awareness of pleasure at seeing her again.

Sophia had lived for the moment of John's return. John Wesley at thirty-three was a good-looking young man in an austere aloof sort of way. Too short to fit the description of a modern handsome man, he nevertheless had regular features with the high forehead of a scholar, a stern chin, and a rather long nose. All were framed by long hair which flowed down over his shoulders.

He dressed neatly. Though he spent little on clothes, those he owned bore the marks of careful attention.

The young Anglican priest was quite different from any man Sophia Hopkey had previously met. Particularly Tom Mellichamp. This turbulent young man, with a tempestuous and passionate nature, was constantly in trouble. In one stormy scene, Tom threatened Sophia, telling her that if she married someone else, it would be a funeral instead of a wedding.

Now in some mysterious manner after the violence of Mellichamp and the alternating oiliness and coarseness of Mr. Causton, she had met a man altogether different. Gentle, considerate, with lofty ideals, one who sought above all to serve God—and he was a bachelor. Though she tried hard to think of him as her "father in God," he was much too young and masculine, and other ideas crept into Sophia's mind.

John Wesley's mistakes were seldom those of the impulsive spirit. Rather they were the unfortunate outcome of a sincere and dedicated man, who with a compulsive thoroughness tried to undertake whatever he felt God required of him.

His study of church history had shown him that many of the saints experienced great difficulty with their appetites. The effort to keep the flesh under control meant a careful choice of simple food. Preparation for his missionary work called for a special effort, and he and Delamotte had decided to make the experiment of abstaining from meat and wine. To their delight they discovered they were thriving on their meager diet.

These eccentricities of Wesley's character bothered Oglethorpe. The simple-minded soldier thought highly of Wesley but saw many problems that could be raised because of John's finicky eating habits which might come to influence the people in a colony who were dependent on the abundant game in the surrounding forests. It would be ridiculous to have the population so preoccupied with fad diets that they ignored the animals so readily available.

So Oglethorpe challenged Wesley to show that a well-rounded normal diet was right for the colonists. Impressed by the logic of the governor's argument, Wesley determined to set an example and sat down to a regular meal of meat and wine. The rich diet upset his stomach which had long been accustomed to simple foods, and they hustled John off to bed.

Even in his misery John became very much aware of the presence of Sophia Hopkey, who had come to take care of him. For five days she gave him her undivided attention. Although he had met her before at the church services, he now saw her through different eyes. Dressed in white, for she had learned that the young minister disliked showy clothes, she looked to John like an angel of mercy.

As she cared for him, she related her story of spiritual difficulty. With characteristic concern Wesley volunteered to become both her spiritual director and teacher.

8.

Life in Frederica

JOHN WESLEY'S MINISTRY was divided between the township of Savannah and the settlement at Fort Frederica, but even while he labored in Savannah, his mind frequently went back to Frederica and the strange assortment of people who lived in that carefully laid out settlement.

Joseph Cannon, aged fifteen, sat at the rough-hewn table, paper in front of him, quill in hand, and sand for blotting the ink at his elbow. His mother had been urging him for days, and when his father finally joined with her to demand action, he capitulated. In his carefully cultivated copperplate handwriting he wrote a letter to his friend Joseph Jessop in England, "We have built us a little room with some boards, which we sawed and built us a chimney in it with clay."

Settled on lot sixteen in the South Ward with a house facing Broad Street, Frederica, David Cannon had quickly erected the "little room" to shelter his wife and two sons. That carefully built little structure stood like a model on display and attracted the attention of the settlers as they walked down Broad Street. They liked what they saw and in short order Cannon was inundated with requests for his services. When Dr. Hawkins and Mr. Davidson planned the most elaborate houses in the colony, they chose Samuel Cannon to build them.

Cannon toiled from dawn to dark assisted regularly by his fifteen-year-old son Joseph and intermittently by ten-year-old Daniel. He saved every penny above expenses in anticipation of opportunities which would present themselves in the burgeoning colony, and on Sundays he tramped around the island searching for a likely spot to develop. Already he had spied out some land on a nearby bluff, and Oglethorpe promised it to him for settlement.

He often sat in the evening and talked with George Spenser, his next-door neighbor, whose house occupied a choice position on the corner of Broad and Barracks Streets. A brickmason by trade, he soon mastered the art of making tabby, the basic masonary material of the fort. Work on the fortifications of Frederica kept him busy, but he spent every spare moment building his own house. And his wife Mary worked right along beside him.

On occasions George would stop suddenly and hold his chest. Mary watched him with anxious eyes. In the tough frontier life every woman needed a man. She tried to warn him but he would wave her off and return to mixing tabby. She had a premonition he would not long live to enjoy his new house, and her womanly intuition later proved correct.

On the western side of the Cannon house stood a vacant lot

and next to it was the home of Will Abbot. Will's well-developed muscles gave mute evidence of his woodcutting skill. When he fell into the rhythmic swing of his axe, he developed such pace that it sounded like a dozen men at work. No mean axeman himself, John Wesley loved to watch Will at work and would periodically relieve him. Will, resting on the grass, could not help but admire the clerical axeman.

But Will had not sailed the Atlantic to spend all his days working at chopping timber. It had become obvious to him on the voyage across that even in this outpost of civilization many people would want to own the finer things of life. And when the *Simmonds* returned to England, she took along a large order from Will.

The front room of Will Abbot's house was gradually stacked with English merchandise. Mary presided over their assortment of what they advertised as "London goods," and the upper class of Frederica dropped by to inspect and purchase, while Will looked to the approaching day when he wouldn't need to cut wood any more.

West of Will Abbot on lot nine, lived Levi Bennett and his wife, Mary. A prosperous couple, they had paid their own passage to America and brought with them an indentured servant named Samuel Lee. Samuel hoped to work out his time and become an independent landowner. He had actually claimed lot thirteen which adjoined that of Will Abbot.

Samuel, as lazy as many of his neighbors were industrious, used every device his fertile mind could concoct to avoid any type of physical labor. John Wesley's closest friend, Thomas Hird, had built a house on lot twelve and it backed up to the Bennett lot. And he could not help but notice the long hours Samuel Lee spent with Mary Bennett. Instead of working, Samuel sat and talked, while Mary did most of the chores for which Samuel had been brought to the colony.

On the day they carried the rough coffin containing the body of Levi Bennett up Broad Street to the burying ground, Samuel took on an air of proprietorship. In what seemed to many an indecently short period, John Wesley was called upon to officiate at the wedding of Samuel Lee and Mary Bennett.

Confirmed now in his idle ways, Samuel sat back and with a sense of self-satisfaction watched while his new wife, with a rare business ability, opened first a tavern and then a store. Each was a successful venture, providing them with good living and increasing influence.

Almost opposite the Samuel Lees lived John Humble on lot eight in the South Ward. When he applied for a place in the new settlement and the clerk asked his trade, he answered, "Laborer." With little opportunity in England, he had never learned a trade. After much uncertainty they finally accepted him. There must be one hewer of wood and drawer of water in the new town.

And while others had looked with fear at the small ship about to sail the Atlantic, the smell of that sea air did something to John. His first glimpse of salt water unleashed a love affair with the sea. That something which made the British men into sea dogs, existed in a large measure in John Humble.

For him the *Simmonds* became a university, and he learned more during those four months at sea than in all his previous years in and out of school. His wife sometimes wondered if he ever slept. He had discovered that members of the crew on duty in the lonely night hours were happy to have an inquisitive companion who studied the compass, the charts, the names of the sails, and the skill of setting them—the strange ways of the sea currents and the intricate processes of navigating the clumsy sailing ship.

And so, while John Humble absentmindedly worked at his laboring job on the fortifications of Frederica, he often threw sticks into the water and watched the way the current flowed.

At quitting time, while other men hurried off to relax under the trees or in their palmetto huts, he scrambled into a rowboat to scull around, heaving out the sounding line and carefully recording the depths of the water.

News of his activity inevitably came to Oglethorpe's attention. Since the water was the only highway out of and into Frederica, he stood in need of a good seaman. And John soon found his place on a boat and ultimately became the first pilot of this new harbor.

John Humble's continuous investigations of the waterfront brought him into contact with Francis Moore, who had been appointed keeper of the stores. Living in a house located on lot twenty of North Ward, Moore had chosen a spot from which he could see the river and also keep an eye on the storehouse for which he was responsible.

Francis not only carefully listed all the stores, but used his recording skill in other ways. He had a natural curiosity which led him to catalog the day-by-day activities of the settlement, and every time he came upon some unusual natural phenomenon, he wrote down a full description. His eyes, long accustomed to an English countryside, were immediately attracted to the Spanish moss which intrigued him, and he wrote, "I observed here a kind of long moss I had never seen before; it grows in great quantities upon the large trees and hangs down three or four yards from the boughs; it gives a noble, ancient, and hoary look to the woods; it is of a whitish-green color, but when dried is black and like horsehair. This the Indians use for wadding their guns and making their couches soft under the skins of beasts which serve them for beds. They use it also for tinder, striking fire by flashing the pans of their guns into a handful of it, and for all other uses where old linen would be necessary."

Moore had his share of worries as keeper of the stores. Supplies sometimes ran low and one crisis arose over bread. Will Allen became the solution to the problem. Will had worked as a baker, and when he and his wife Elizabeth joined the group, Will was indentured to the trustees. As irate settlers complained to Oglethorpe that they needed bread not flour, he sent for Will who came up with an idea.

Oglethorpe ordered some of the men taken off house construction and set them to work under Will's direction. They built an oven, and Oglethorpe announced that whoever wanted bread should take his allotment of flour to Will. The baker would return to them the same weight in bread, keeping the difference made by adding water and salt. Moore noted, "Fresh bread was a great comfort to the people."

As John Wesley thought about the population of Frederica, he often wondered what the trustees had in mind when they chose the men for the expedition. Richard White who lived on lot 35 of the South Ward was a hatter and had great difficulty in settling down to building and farming activities. Fortuitously his next-door neighbor, John Henney, a cooper by trade, needed an assistant. Henney discovered the residents of Frederica wanted barrels either built or repaired, and since fairly good water could be reached by digging down about six feet, barrels provided an excellent casing for the insides of the wells. The two men worked industriously on the barrels, but White's blistered hands were constant reminders that he had once known an easier way of life. So he only worked as a cooper until he could accumulate enough capital to open a store.

A stroll along Barracks Street in the North Ward confronted John Wesley with the bewildering variety of his parishioners. Ambrose Tackner, a smoldering volcano of a man, German by birth, had on the voyage across the Atlantic taught John Wesley the tongue by which he hoped to communicate with the Moravians and the Salzburgers.

While in one of the periodic fits of depression, Tackner had attended the shipboard church services and John optimistically hoped he might be his first convert. But nothing came of this, and Tackner's outbursts of temper seemed to increase in violence. In his struggles to reason with Tackner John had some moments of apprehension during which he came to believe that Tackner had the capacity to commit cold-blooded murder.

Although the eighteenth-century woman had few legal rights, the Fort Frederica women exercised a remarkable influence over the affairs of the colony. The vain Mrs. Perkins represented the worst aspects of Frederica's feminine population. Despite her husband's deteriorating finances she thought only of herself. Sometime later Count Egmont wrote about Samuel Perkins, "He owed 600 pounds but his wife must go in silk."

With such a diversity of personalities it was small wonder that a series of crises left the settlement in a state of turmoil and laid heavy pressures on John Wesley and his fellow workers.

9.

Fleas: No Sleep

May 22–June 23, 1736

METHODIST CIRCUIT RIDERS made an indelible imprint on the religious life of the American frontier. Bibles in saddle-bags, these ecclesiastical frontiersmen were in the van of the movement across the country. Unlike their fellows who ventured into the wilderness to clear and cultivate the land and build new towns, they sought to harvest a spiritual crop. Using this technique they perpetuated the spirit of John Wesley, the irrepressible itinerant.

This first and greatest of all the circuit riders followed a circuit with preaching points in Savannah and the one-hundred-mile distant Fort Frederica. The peculiar topography of the country called for him sometimes to ride a horse, like his latter day successors, but more frequently to cling to a bucking boat. The Georgia coast between Savannah and Frederica is a gigantic maze of water, land, and marshes. Here is a tortuous labyrinth of waterways to frustrate either the sailor or the landsman trying to find his way through the mass of rivers, inlets, bays, islands, and swamps. A boat provided the only practical means of transportation.

Frederica brought more than its quota of difficulties, but Savannah also had its problems. The tug-o-war between the two settlements kept Wesley constantly on the move.

Mr. Parker, a sawyer by trade, was loud-mouthed and given to drinking. Since coming to Savannah, he had curried favor with Causton and was appointed second bailiff of the colony. He and his wife requested Mr. Wesley to baptize their new baby.

John called on Mrs. Parker and explained that he followed the literal instructions of the Prayer Book and only baptized by trine immersion, which meant dipping the child three times in water.

The suggestion horrified Mrs. Parker, "Neither Mr. Parker or I will consent to our child being dipped."

The minister pointed out the alternative, "If you certify that your child is weak, it will suffice to pour water upon it."

"My child is not weak, but I am resolved it shall not be dipped."

The Parkers had their child baptized elsewhere.

One day Charles appeared without warning in Savannah. The governor was sending him to England to report to the trustees. This meant that someone must go minister to the colonists in Frederica. Now that Oglethorpe had built his house at St. Simons and taken up residence there, it had become increasingly important. Talking it over with Ingham, John and he concluded they must serve Frederica in turn, and that John should take the first stint.

Walking overland to avoid part of the tedious river trip, John boarded the boat at Thunderbolt. The going was rough because of a severe storm; however, the industrious John refused to let the wind and weather interfere with his work. He worked on his German, translated part of the Greek Testament, took turns at the oars, wrote in his diary, and sang. He also noted in his diary "verses" which indicates his work of translating some of the Moravian hymns. One of these reflects the stormy voyage and reads:

Though waves and storms go o'er my head
  Though strength, and health, and friends be gone,
Though joys be withered all and dead,
  Though every comfort be withdrawn,
On this my steadfast soul relies,
  Father, Thy mercy never dies!

At six o'clock on Sunday morning the boat arrived in Frederica, and the governor, hearing of his arrival, asked to see him. A deeply concerned Oglethorpe told Wesley of the difficult situation facing the settlers. The Spaniards, threatening to attack, had superior numbers and might easily push the colonists off St. Simons Island.

As John patiently listened, Oglethorpe's anxiety gradually dissipated. The solemn Wesley never failed to reassure the harassed governor. Regaining his composure, Oglethorpe steered the conversation to Savannah, Miss Fosset, and Miss Sophia. John responded warmly and talked at length, particularly about Miss Sophia.

From this conversation with the governor, Wesley realized his responsibility lay in helping to reassure the colonists, so he started a schedule of intensive visitation throughout Frederica.

Pretty Mrs. Welch poured out a story of her illogical fears to John. From there he hurried on to visit with Mr. Horton and Major Richards who in the course of negotiating with the Spaniards under a flag of truce had been taken prisoner. Only through the resourcefulness of Oglethorpe had their return been arranged. John listened to their story and tried to encourage them. Next he conducted a communion service, and had the Germans meet with him for a time of singing and prayers.

In the days that followed the Spanish threat gradually subsided as news trickled through that the expeditionary force had withdrawn to Florida. The colony settled down to at least a modicum of normality.

John had no high estimate of sleep. For him it seemed as a narcotic that stole away his time. By careful training he tried to reduce the hours spent in this drugged condition. He slept in the oddest places—on a boat, in a storehouse, in the corner of a hut. An early riser, he liked to get off to sleep fairly early in the evening, but in the storehouse in Frederica malevolent forces seemed to conspire to upset his rest. A plague of fleas had invaded the storehouse, and he laconically noted in his diary, "Fleas: no sleep."

The whole problem of accommodations had grown intolerable. He conducted church services on the third floor of the storehouse. It was the only public meeting place in the fort, and many of the town idlers gathered there. The services were held at eight and eleven in the morning and at three and six in the evening. To many of the settlers this seemed to be overdoing it.

The conflict over a meeting place may be the key to understanding the strange and unusual enthusiasm that took hold of Wesley at this time. Entitled to a lot, he decided to build a house, and with as much ardor as he had ever shown for any enterprise, he commenced the building process. He urged on the indentured servants as they labored, and periodically laid aside his cassock to work like a common laborer.

No sooner had they roofed the house than Wesley moved in and neatly stacked his books and meager possessions in one corner. At last he had a private meeting place for his "company."

Before leaving Savannah he had started a new movement in which the more serious-minded of his church members formed themselves into a society to meet regularly. Now at Frederica he launched a similar project.

With the completion of the house on the evening of June 10, 1736, John decided to hold a meeting that night. Present were himself and Charles Delamotte and one outsider, Mark Hird.

The following Sunday Mrs. Mackay, Phoebe Hird, and Betty Hazle gathered for the first meeting of the company. They discussed the purpose of the gathering, began to read Law's *Christian Perfection,* and finally closed by singing a hymn.

The groups met on Wednesdays and Fridays, and on the Wednesday following the first meeting Wesley divided his people into two groups. Mr. Reed led the men and Phoebe Hird led the women. As routine as this might seem, the plan of organization represented a historic departure from established Church of England procedure. High churchman John Wesley had appointed two lay people, a man and a woman, to lead groups within the church at Frederica, thus beginning the revolutionary practice of using lay people as church leaders. The attitude ultimately led to Methodism giving a new emphasis to the place and role of the laymen in church life.

Other forces pressed in on him, but none were more abrasive or symbolic of the powers of evil than Mrs. Hawkins. She continued to be the bane of his existence. When John had arrived on this visit, Oglethorpe told him of all the trouble caused by Beata Hawkins. Memories of this interview made him defensive, and when she sent a message that she wished to see him, he ignored the request.

The following Sunday he took his afternoon stroll into the woods and on his return, momentarily forgetting Mrs. Hawkins, he absent-mindedly turned down Broad Street, passing the Hawkins' residence. Beata called to him, and seeing Dr. Hawkins looking over her shoulder, he went on into the house. Dr. Hawkins, as the physician of the colony, had come to feel the challenge of John's penchant for prescribing medicine for sick people and drew him into a discussion of nutrition. In no other field did John feel so confident, and he held forth on the merits of a bread diet. Dr. Hawkins looked at him in mock alarm and then quoted what he regarded as unassailable authorities, producing evidence that peas were the ideal food.

Unconvinced by Hawkins' argument, John nevertheless found it very agreeable to talk to these two in this friendly way. So much so that at their express request he was back again the next evening when they were both "very serious" and "open." He might have even stayed later if it had not been for his promise to assist Mr. Lassel in drawing up his will.

The good relationship proved to be a lull before the storm. Beata had entered upon another round of quarrels with her neighbors. When John remonstrated with her, she flew into a fit of anger that drove him from the house.

He returned later to find her in the midst of a violent quarrel with her husband. Dr. Hawkins stamped out of the house. Beata's anger subsided as she sat and talked with John who was waiting somewhat apprehensively for her husband's return. As the doctor reentered the house, she flew into another rage and John retreated.

The following Tuesday evening, at the Hawkins' invitation,

John called again at their house. Beata talked seriously, but when John insisted on pointing out the danger of ungovernable rage, she lost her temper, and in a dramatic moment shouted at him, "Mr. Wesley, I utterly renounce your friendship."

Her irate words ringing in his ears, John returned home, thankful for a place of refuge.

Oglethorpe who had made a quick trip to Savannah unexpectedly returned on Saturday June 19th. The governor's furrowed brow told John that his stay in Savannah had worried him, and when John Burk, who had been in the governor's party, came by to visit, John questioned him. Burk talked freely about the problems of Savannah. It seemed that Causton's work as a magistrate left much to be desired, and Oglethorpe was disillusioned about both the man and his work.

As with many another minister, Saturday night meant preparing sermons for the following day, and listening to Burk's description of Savannah fired up John's latent prophetic abilities.

Church attendance at Frederica fluctuated, the number present being affected by many factors, but Oglethorpe's presence always guaranteed a good congregation. Sunday the 20th saw the governor at morning worship with the chapel in the north storehouse nicely filled.

With the image of Savannah's degeneration before him, John launched into a "state of the settlement" message. Without sparing details or persons he compared Frederica with what he considered to be Christian standards. As he warmed to his subject, John raised his voice to declare that, "Righteousness exalteth a nation but sin is a reproach to any people." And as he saw it, Frederica would never really prosper until it paid attention to its religious obligation. However, not everything was wrong. John commended the governor on the order that no one should profane the Sabbath, and that all fishing and hunting on Sunday must be stopped at once.

Having delivered his soul, John had a sense of a job well done, but that sermon infuriated many of the townspeople. As if it were not enough to be living so many miles from civilization, now they were to be deprived of a few simple pleasures because of the governor's blue law which they were certain had originated because of Wesley's influence.

Horton, who had run the settlement during Oglethorpe's absence and felt the sermon indirectly attacked him, was particularly antagonistic. He stalked out of church with head high, ignoring John. And a little later when the preacher approached a group standing by the fort, Horton turned and walked down Broad Street in a huff.

John had always prized "openness" so when he encountered Horton later, he asked him the reason for his attitude. The free-living settler looked him in the eye and said, "I like nothing you do. All your sermons are satires upon particular persons; therefore, I will never hear you more; and all the people are of my mind, for we won't hear ourselves abused.

"Besides, they say they are Protestants. But as for you, they cannot tell what religion you are of. They never heard of such religion before. They do not know what to make of it. There is neither man nor woman in the town who minds a word you say. And so you may preach long enough; but nobody will come to hear you."

As the recital proceeded, Horton's face grew redder. But after the tirade had run its course, he stopped and stood there waiting for John's answer. Wesley, wise enough to see the futility of trying to reason with a man in the grip of such strong emotion, replied, "I thank you for your candor and openness Mr. Horton," and he turned and walked back toward the houses.

John, planning to leave Frederica on the next day, puzzled over the whole situation in the colony and became vividly aware of the words from the Scripture lesson for the day: "Whereunto shall I liken the men of this generation? They are like unto children sitting in the marketplace, and saying, We have piped unto you, and ye have not danced; we have mourned to you, and ye have not wept. For John the Baptist came neither eating bread nor drinking wine; and ye say, he hath a devil. The Son of Man is come eating and drinking; and ye say, Behold a gluttonous man, and a wine-bibber, a friend of publicans and sinners!"

Jesus' description of his generation seemed to be particularly applicable to the people of Frederica. Like spoiled children playing games, it didn't matter whether the message was presented in a winsome or serious way they refused to respond. He was not exactly sorry to be leaving the outpost for a while.

10.

Those Greek Words

July 23–September 1, 1736

A LONELY JOHN stood at the dock in Savannah. Weary of all the intrigue of the town and the pressures of the Causton house, Sophia had decided to visit her friend Miss Fosset in Frederica. Watching the periagua moving downstream, he waved farewell, starkly aware of the irony of his situation. While living in Frederica, his thoughts persistently turned to Savannah. Even building a house and a garden could not obliterate the memory of Sophia. Now after being back with her for two short months, she was on her way to Frederica from which he had come.

An uneasiness had descended upon the whole colony. A Spanish attack still threatened at any moment. Savannah and Frederica were alive with rumors, and the people lived in constant fear. John shared many of the same concerns but had the added burden of Mrs. Hawkins. Even though a hundred miles away, she still pursued him with an unending stream of letters. John, always courteous and considerate, spent long hours in answering her unending stream of questions.

Sunday, July 25, Charles preached his last sermon in Savannah before leaving for England on his special mission for the governor. And then John accompanied him to Charleston. Because of an extremely rough sea it took them five days to make the trip.

When John returned to Savannah after a two week's absence, he discovered that the governor had gone to Frederica. And since John had brought important letters from Charleston for Oglethorpe, it was agreed that he should hurry on to the fort.

To shorten the journey he walked overland to Thunderbolt where he could board the boat. A torrential downpour wet his clothes but could not dampen his spirits. Though he would not admit it openly, he had missed Sophia while in Savannah and the anticipation of reunion brightened the journey.

He arrived at Frederica just in time to catch Oglethorpe before he departed for Fort George. The governor thanked him for the mail and then asked about Miss Sophia. John readily admitted he was anxious to see her again, and upon leaving Oglethorpe, he hurried to the Hird's house where Sophia was staying. And following a joyful reunion, they had a long and serious talk.

Whenever John had something to say, a peculiar intensity came into Sophia's blue eyes. Whatever was important to John was equally important to her. And on this occasion the discussion turned to a new project into which John had thrown himself. John had discovered that many of the songs the Moravians sang had been passed on orally, and he was working at reducing them to writing. Gradually a repertoire grew, and with it an idea. Why not prepare a selection of the best hymns for the use in the societies?

But how would he decide which hymns to include? He needed help. Why not Sophia? So they set aside one whole Saturday to work on the project. One by one John read the hymns to Sophia. By the end of the day they had made the first selections of what was to become the *Collection of Psalms and Hymns.* It had been a good day and John brought it to a conclusion by reading evening prayers for Sophia.

Monday found them working together on his Journal again. Breaking away to do pastoral work, he became conscious of a fever which put him to bed for two restless days.

Friday, August 20th, dawned much like any other August day—hot, sticky, and plagued with insects. Sand flies continued to torture the settlers, and John frequently rose in the night to light a fire to smoke out the offensive insects. And with Oglethorpe away, the antagonism of the settlers grew more blatant.

Despite an attack of fever, the conscientious John arose at 4:45 in the morning, but after praying thirty minutes his weakened body gave up, and he collapsed in sleep. Nevertheless, he aroused himself for morning prayers and felt encouraged when he saw Miss Sophia sitting in her usual seat.

John was now eating his meals at the Hirds', an arrangement which provided him with better food and more time with Sophia. Following lunch he would sit around with Miss Sophia and Mark Hird singing hymns.

It now developed that John was spending the biggest proportion of his days with Sophia. Without intending to, he had drifted into a situation that had all the earmarks of potential trouble. But other eyes watched and more intently than those of Mrs. Hawkins, who carefully noted every time Wesley met

Sophia at the Hird house, the length of time he spent reading to her, and the strolls they took under the moss-laden oaks.

Recurrent attacks of fever laid John low. Surges of heat gave way to fits of shivering. He blamed the vapors from the nearby marshes for his condition, blissfully unaware that amid those tormenting mosquitoes had come a female anopheles, putting him at the mercy of the malaria parasite.

Struggling to stay on his feet, he knew he needed medication. A decoction of the bark would do it. So he walked down Broad Street to the Hawkins residence to see the doctor. To his chagrin Mrs. Hawkins opened the door and gave him a warm welcome, urging him to sit down. Dr. Hawkins would be back shortly.

John Wesley had an unusually even temper and could withstand the greatest of adversities without complaint, but sitting in the Hawkins house with Beata edging closer, he mentally recalled how much time he had spent with this couple. The situation riled him because he had recently heard that Dr. Hawkins had spread stories around the town about him and Charles.

"Mrs. Hawkins, I am concerned about the way some people have been treating me. While I might expect this from some of the settlers, I am disturbed to find Dr. Hawkins, who I really looked upon as a friend, joining with them."

Beata looked startled, "How do you mean my husband has treated you badly?"

"By showing one of my brother's letters to a number of people. If he had any complaint, he should have come to me with it."

Her lips tightened, "All the women in the town are uneasy and affronted by those two Greek words in the letter. They think they are a reflection on them. Pray tell me, to whom do they refer?"

John and Charles had long followed the custom of using a

code in their letters so that the choicest parts would be kept secret. At times they wrote certain sentences in Latin or in Greek. When Charles had written John about his suspicions of some of the promiscuous activities of Mrs. Hawkins and Mrs. Welch, he wrote the statements in Greek so that it could be read, he hoped, only by John. However, the letter had been intercepted, copied, and passed around the town. Charles had not mentioned either Mrs. Hawkins or Mrs. Welch in the letter, hence the uproar, particularly among the women of the colony, many of whom thought they were the subjects under discussion.

Beata Hawkins had maneuvered John into a difficult position. From being the attacker, he now found himself on the defensive. He could see that no simple answer would satisfy her. "Whatever was in that letter was written by Charles, not by me, so it is not my responsibility. Moreover, the situation is now changed and Charles is of a different opinion now than he was then."

John paused, but Beata wouldn't let him out of the corner . . . "But those Greek words."

He plunged in, "Those words were not meant to describe all the women in town; they refer only to you and Mrs. Welch."

Mrs. Hawkins jumped to her feet and shouted, "John Wesley, you are a villain, a scoundrel, a pitiful rascal."

At this critical moment the door opened to admit Dr. Hawkins. Words tumbled through Beata's thin lips, "He has just told me that dog his brother Charles meant me by those damned words."

Hawkins' distaste for Wesley had been building up over the months. He had objected to all the time Beata spent with John and the never ending conferences about religion. All his resentment at last found a focal point. He let fly with a blast of abuse, and Beata joined in. For a few moments they tried to outshout each other, using coarse language that offended

John's sensitive ears, and brought tears to his eyes.

The sight of John's tears seemed to infuriate Hawkins even more. Looking over to Beata, he shouted, "We'll unfrock the pair of them."

John wiped the tears and drew himself up with simple dignity, "The sooner you have us unfrocked the better, I will go immediately to report the whole matter to Mr. Oglethorpe."

With a heavy heart John walked across town to the governor's residence where he related the entire experience. The governor suggested John and Dr. and Mrs. Hawkins meet with him that evening after prayers.

The conference was far from satisfactory. The agitated Hawkins kept interrupting and used such intemperate language in relating his version of the affair that Oglethorpe was compelled to rebuke him.

Trying to adjudicate impartially, Oglethorpe delivered his verdict, "It seems to me that Rev. Charles Wesley ought never have written that letter, however, it would be wrong to hold Rev. John Wesley responsible for what his brother has done, and I am disappointed at the way in which you have attacked Mr. Wesley. Consider this as a reprimand. You are all dismissed."

John rose early Saturday morning after a night plagued with mosquitoes and memories of the dispute with the Hawkins. Walking along Barracks Street, he met Mr. Horton. Anxious to build good relations with him, John stopped to talk. In the grip of a bad mood, Horton let him know in no uncertain terms that he felt John was spending too much time prying into other people's affairs. He had betrayed people who trusted him, and it seemed that he was determined to create all the trouble he could.

The recital sickened John, and he said, "Why on earth do you think I would do this sort of thing?"

Thoroughly wound up, Horton shouted, "I believe in a

morning when you say your prayers, you resolve against it; but by the time you have been abroad two hours, all your resolutions are vanished, and you can't be easy till you're at it again."

John watched him as he stomped off, and was certainly not prepared for Mrs. Welch who picked that particular moment to call out to him, "Mr. Wesley, Mr. Wesley. What do you mean by saying I am an adultress?"

John stood there stunned. A small crowd quickly gathered, and Mrs. Welch, filled with indignation, addressed him with the profanity of a fishwife. Mustering what dignity he could, John walked off down the street to the shelter of his house, where he sat and tried to regather his thoughts.

A puzzled John, contemplating the complex situation involving Mrs. Welch and Dr. and Mrs. Hawkins, decided that the best thing for him to do was to consider them as dead. If they were no longer alive in his mind, he could devote himself to the "cure of souls" and leave them entirely to their own devices.

But he wasn't to be done with them so easily. Feeling thankful for the new tranquility, John was writing in his journal one warm Sunday afternoon when there came a knock at the door. When he answered it, he found himself face-to-face with Mrs. Hawkins' servant. The woman handed him a note which he read, "Mr. Wesley, I must speak to you about a matter of great importance."

He asked, "Do you know what it is your mistress wants to talk to me about?"

"No."

On the horns of a dilemma John tried to decide what to do. Every vestige of commonsense told him to stay away from this designing female, but the priest won the battle over the man, and he murmured, as much to himself as to the servant, "If a parishioner desires my company, I must go."

He hesitated for a moment, then admonished the servant,

"Be sure you don't go out of the room and leave us alone."

John's fears were reinforced when upon arriving at the Hawkins' home, the servant ushered him into the lady's bedroom. Standing grim-faced with arms behind her back, she nodded toward the bed, "Sir, sit down."

Bolt upright, strange misgivings about having come pulsating through him, John watched her moving ever closer. Suddenly the mysteriously hidden right hand snaked forth brandishing a pistol.

In measured tones she said, "Sir, you have wronged me. I will shoot you through the head this moment with a brace of balls."

Just for good measure she drew her left hand from its hiding place. In it she wielded an evil-looking pair of scissors.

John reacted instinctively and grabbed at the pistol. They struggled. Beata fought like a wildcat, and John fell backwards on the bed.

Beata shouted and swore, "Villain, dog, let go of my hands. I'm going to have your hair and your heart's blood."

John continued to struggle with Mrs. Hawkins. Where was that servant? He couldn't call out and have people running in to find him in this compromising predicament.

At last the maid's frightened face appeared at the door. Beata spotted her. In a voice of authority she shouted, "Bring me a knife, if you don't I'll use it on you later."

Frightened and trembling the servant stood rooted to the floor. Two men servants attracted by the noise put their heads in the door, and to them she shouted, "Seize hold of this man; he is attacking your mistress."

The new arrivals just stood there, as embarrassed and perplexed as their female counterpart.

Banging on the door saved the day. The flustered maid was relieved to open it and see Mr. Davidson, the next-door neighbor, and a constable, with John's friend, Mr. Reed, demanding to know what was happening.

John called out, "Please take Mrs. Hawkins by the arms and remove her from me."

As they moved towards her, Dr. Hawkins came rushing through the doorway. "What is that scoundrel doing in my house?" he shouted. Then turning to Reed and Davidson he warned, "Don't you dare lay a hand on my wife."

Mrs. Hawkins took the cue and burst into action trying to bite John's flailing arms. She succeeded in tearing the sleeve out of his cassock and sunk her teeth into his forearm.

Two other men had now pushed into the house, and anxious to avoid any more publicity, Hawkins entered the fray. Seizing hold of Beata by the waist he hauled her off the unfortunate John.

Gathering what dignity he could, Wesley retreated from the house and made a beeline to Governor Oglethorpe to report his humiliating experience. The long-suffering governor sent for Dr. and Mrs. Hawkins, but he rubbed salt into John's wounds by inviting Horton to be present.

Beata entered a spirited defense of her actions. Mr. Wesley had treated her shabbily and refused to make amends, so she had attacked him.

Oglethorpe, after letting everybody talk at length, reprimanded both the doctor and his wife, and with an exhortation that they behave themselves in the future, he dismissed the whole group.

Returning to his house, John fell into a low mood. Coming across on the ship he'd had such high hopes for his ministry to Dr. and Mrs. Hawkins. Now he wondered at the enigma of Beata. She had seemed so open and responsive on several occasions and now this.

John slept in his own house that uneasy night. His friends,

Mark Hird and Reed, both concerned for his safety, also slept there, keeping guard, just in case.

If John and Oglethorpe had hoped the incident was closed, they hoped in vain. The Hawkins' story had made the rounds of the settlement and with repetition it grew beyond recognition. John Wesley had attacked Beata Hawkins in her bedroom. Moreover, he was about to sneak off to Savannah.

John's house was as busy as a pedestrain crosswalk. Some came to bid him farewell; others to plead with him not to depart, still others inquiring as to the true facts of the episode. Almost tormented to distraction, John wrote to the governor:

> Sir, I choose to write rather than speak, that I may not say too much. I find it is utterly impossible anything should be kept secret unless both parties are resolved upon it. What fell out yesterday is already known to every family in Frederica; but to many it has been represented in such a light that 'tis easy to know whence the representation comes. Now, Sir, what can I do more? Though I have given my reputation to God, I must not absolutely neglect it. The treatment I have met with was not barely an assault; you know one part of it was felony. I can't see what I can do but desire an open hearing in the face of all my countrymen of this place. If you (to whom I can gladly entrust my life and my all in this land) are excepted against as partial, let a jury be impanelled, and upon a full inquiry determine what such breaches of the law deserve.
>
> I am, Sir, Your obliged and obedient Servant.
>
> John Wesley

The letter brought action, but to John's disappointment Oglethorpe had handed over the affair to Horton. Horton said a jury would be empaneled if John insisted but proceeded to deliver a long lecture on the importance of unity in the colony. John replied that he would not insist if the Hawkins stopped spreading their stories. So another interview was held with

Oglethorpe and Dr. and Mrs. Hawkins. The difficult hour concluded with an agreement that neither party speak to or about the other. The agreement brought a sense of relief to John.

Normally an incident like the Hawkins episode would have been the subject of discussion in Frederica for weeks, but suddenly a far more significant event overshadowed. The lookout shouted warning of an approaching Spanish warship, the *Havanna*. The Captain, Don Antonio de Arredondo, came ashore with great ceremony to announce that he was representing the king of Spain and had come to negotiate with Governor Oglethorpe.

Arrangements had to be hastily made. Captain Gascoigne went to nearby Jekyll Island and erected tents for the captain and his party, and the *Havanna* anchored in the stream separating St. Simons and Jekyll. The Spaniards remained for seven days, and on each of these days Oglethorpe and leading personalities of the colony visited with them for discussions and negotiations.

Rumors raced around the settlement. Many of the people felt, and not without justification, that the Spaniards were simply spying out the land and trying to discover the strength of the fortifications. After the ship's departure, guards were carefully posted, and the settlers braced themselves for a possible attack.

Diligently working at his pastoral duties, John received a message that Mrs. Patterson lay dangerously ill. He walked to the Patterson home and tried to bring spiritual solace to the troubled woman. Another visitor came by. Mrs. Hawkins. As she entered the room, a thousand thoughts rushed through John's mind. But he had learned his lesson. He gave the curtest nod, read a prayer, and departed.

11.

"Ah, My Frederica"

September 2–October 23, 1736

THE KING'S INDEPENDENT COMPANY from South Carolina under the command of Lieutenant Delegal, which manned the fort at the south end of St. Simons Island, had its own chaplain officially designated to help bolster the morale of the unit.

Mr. Dison, the chaplain, was by unanimous opinion, as unworthy a man as ever wore the cloth. He had little desire to remain in isolated St. Simons and periodically roamed off to visit other outposts of colonists and carried on his dubious activities away from the prying eyes of the St. Simons residents. When John arrived at the settlement in August, 1736, Dison immediately volunteered to conduct services in Savannah, if John would look after the spiritual welfare of the Independent Company.

Happy for an opportunity to remain near Miss Sophia, John had readily agreed to the plan. But before long stories about Mr. Dison began to filter back to John. He had turned into a "Marrying Sam," performing hasty weddings without calling the banns, had spread malicious stories about John's behavior and preaching, and was christening children in private houses rather than in the church.

Telling Sophia goodby, John boarded a sloop, and set out for Savannah. He stopped only to preach at Skidaway Island and then hurried on to his destination.

John went immediately to Dison's lodgings and faced him with the charges. Dison denied everything except the private christening of babies, in which he acknowledged he had been wrong. John characteristically lamented, "O discipline! where art thou to be found. Not in England, nor as yet in America."

After eleven days in Savannah his thoughts were already turning back to Frederica and Sophia. He sat down with Ingham and Delamotte to discuss the Frederica situation. Some minister of the gospel should be there. Who would it be? To John's relief they decided on him.

One incident might have worried a more worldly-minded man. Before he left for the fort, John called on Mr. Causton. During the course of their discussion, the chief magistrate encouraged Wesley to fill him in on the latest news from Frederica—the ups and downs of life in the outpost, relationships with the Indians, and the ever-present threat of the Spaniards.

"What commands do you have for Miss Sophia?"

Her uncle replied, "The girl will never be easy till she is married."

"She is too much afflicted to have a thought of it."

Causton smiled, "I'll trust a woman for that. There is no other way."

John was perplexed and highlighted a difficulty, "But there are few here you would think fit for her."

"Let him be but an honest man—an honest good man; I don't care whether he has a groat. I can give them maintenance."

"Sir, what directions do you give me with regard to her?"

"I give her up to you. Do what you will with her. Take her into your own hands. Promise her what you will. I will make it good."

That evening Mrs. Causton roared with laughter as her husband recounted the conversation. This must surely be the broadest hint John had ever received.

As he sat in the Frederica-bound boat, John pondered Causton's words about his niece. What did he mean? To John they were very clear and plain: Causton wanted his niece prepared so that she would be ready for marriage. Her character must be developed and her mind stimulated. He must work harder on Sophia's education.

While the boat maneuvered for the landing at the fort, John watched the shore. Mark Hird alone waited to greet him. Where was Miss Sophia?

Once ashore, Mark Hird took John to one side and related the dismal story. One of his most noble converts had defected. Morning and evening prayers had been discontinued. The colony was as heathen as any Indian village on the nearby mainland.

John threw up his hands, "In trouble in trouble, alas in trouble. Ah, my Frederica."

Worst of all was the case of Miss Sophia. After all his fond anticipations he found her with only a shadow of her former spiritual vitality. During his absence she had been one of the first to quit attendance at morning and evening prayers. She had changed.

After the final showdown between John Wesley and the Hawkins, Beata had developed a new and all-consuming interest. The Hawkins had decided to build a house, the most elaborate, permanent private dwelling in Frederica. She hoped to look down proudly on her less fortunate fellow settlers from the magnificence of her new home.

Driven on by her insatiable desire for attention, Beata kept after her husband, causing him to alter and enlarge his plans, until he built her a handsome three-story house. And, as was the custom of the time, the houses were built in duplex fashion —a carry-over from a style currently in vogue in most of England's crowded cities. The Davidsons joined with the Hawkins in this building project.

The foundations and inner walls of these houses were built of tabby, a concrete made from crushed oyster shells. The exterior walls were of brick. A common wall, known as a "party wall," joined the two residences.

Why the Hawkins built a house tied to that of the Davidsons we will never know. The two families were as unlike in values and in attitude and spirit as the houses were similar. A chairman by trade, Samuel Davidson had been selected to come to the colony to make musket stocks. He had a wife and three children. Industrious and of good character, he was a close friend and supporter of the Wesleys.

And contemporary records show that while Dr. Hawkins occupied an influential position and ran a successful medical practice, he and his wife were thoroughly disliked by the settlers. At one time or another most of the outstanding settlers had altercations with him.

It was small wonder that difficulties ultimately arose between the Davidsons and the Hawkins, and, as would be expected, the aggressors were the Hawkins. One long quarrel centered around the roof. After a time, the Davidsons wanted to renew their roof, but after first agreeing to go ahead, Mr. Hawkins decided he would have none of it. The argument grew hotter and reached a stalemate with all work halted. Davidson, now literally without a roof over his head, was compelled to move his family into a stable.

In the earlier encounter with Charles Wesley when Hawkins had fired off a gun during the church service, Davidson who was also a constable had arrested him and escorted him to jail. So the party wall between the two houses came to symbolize the division of the settlement between the pro- and anti-Wesley forces.

Although Charles was the major target for the hostility of Frederica's inhabitants, many of them were as much opposed to John's puritanical ideas. Some would never forget the scene at the Cockspur Island landing. After John's prayers, Oglethorpe had appointed officers to take charge and departed for the mainland. Feeling their religious responsibilities discharged, the people had turned to more earthly pleasures. Some traders from North Carolina had secretly sold them a good supply of rum. And within a few hours the beach scene had become a drunken orgy.

John, returning from a walk of exploration across the island, had gazed at the scene with incredulity. He felt like Moses coming down from the mountain when he discovered the people he had hoped to lead into the promised land worshiping the golden calf. Like the patriarch he had felt the need for drastic action. Gathering the few sober people and taking axes, they staved in the ends of the rum barrels. Needless to say, this did absolutely nothing toward improving Wesley's stature with the colonists.

During the early days of the settlement a number of fires proved the first palmetto huts to be fire traps. Every ambitious settler then aimed at building a fireproof house, and tabby was the ideal material. The remarkably simple construction involved mixing lime, sand, and water with oyster shells added as the aggregate to give it strength. After it had been mixed, the moist material was poured into forms and allowed to set. Once it had dried hard, the workmen removed the forms and positioned them for the next layer, so the wall grew six inches at a time.

Lime, the main ingredient in the tabby, came from the abundant oyster shells garnered from Indian mounds. First a layer of wood, then oyster shells, then wood, and so on, until the high mound of successive layers stood ready for firing. The heat of the burning fire removed the moisture from the shells leaving the valuable lime.

Shell burnings were festive occasions for the colonists. Once lit, the mounds burned throughout the night. At these social events the musicians played while the people danced, ate, drank, and socialized. From time to time some of the men raked and stoked the burning materials, making sure the shells were properly baked.

Frederica's favorite lime kiln was located about four miles from the town, and on one particular night of the lime burning, the girls had gone on down the trail with their escorts. Men carried baskets of food on their shoulders, and anxious mothers kept a watchful eye on their children. And Sophia sitting in her palmetto hut choked back her tears. No one had thought to invite her. She belonged to the "company." But because she spent so much time with the John Wesley group, the Hawkins faction identified her with the puritanical standards that so irked the settlers. The result was that she now found herself shunned by the power structure of the settlement.

Later, while discussing this with John, she made it clear that the whole dreary life of the colonies palled on her and announced her intention of returning to England at the earliest possible opportunity. She had made up her mind, and nothing could change it.

In his methodical manner John recorded all this in his journal. His writing, normally so neat, underwent a change. There was only one other place in his diary where the writing was as shaky as this and that was the portion of the journal which he wrote aboard the *Simmonds* in the midst of the storm coming across the Atlantic. The tempest within was causing even his normal steady hand to tremble violently.

But John developed what he hoped was a remedy for Sophia's condition. He had her come by his house where he spent a considerable amount of time reading devotional classics to her. Conscious of Mr. Causton's admonition, he worked harder for her spiritual restoration. Despite all this, he could not change her mind.

As a last resort, he urged upon her the importance of her friendship for him. He would miss her so much.

That did it. Sophia burst into tears, looked at him and said, "Now my resolution begins to stagger."

Oglethorpe returned to Frederica. As the governor's boat pulled into its moorings, John stood with several of the settlers waiting to welcome him. For some strange reason when Oglethorpe stepped to the top of the stairs, he paid no attention to John but went over to greet Horton. The two walked off talking together.

What was the meaning of this gratuitous snub? Humiliated and distressed, John made his way over to the Hird house to call on Miss Sophia. He told her she might as well leave for England. His influence with the governor was gone, and he could do nothing to help her if she remained in the colony.

All of Sophia's maternal instincts came into focus. With a

note of confidence and hope, she said, "Sir, you encouraged me in my greatest trials. Be not discouraged in your own. Fear nothing. If Mr. Oglethorpe will not, God will help you."

The misunderstanding with the governor was cleared up, but John was not particularly sorry it had happened. He'd seen Sophia in her true light. She was a comforter and encourager.

12.

Epic Journey

October 24–31, 1736

OGLETHORPE SOMETIMES WONDERED which was his worst enemy, France, Spain, or the settlers. Instead of working industriously to build the new utopia, they all too frequently lapsed back into old ways and tried to exploit each other with little regard for the idealistic objectives of their colony.

Like the rank and file colonists, the leaders, too, were a mixed bag. Some were honest and competent, but many of them, like Causton, only aimed at feathering their own nests. This only complicated the process of getting the infant settlement off to a good start.

Oglethorpe liked John Wesley. No matter what their differences might have been, he never for a moment doubted John's basic integrity. If anything, the priest was too conscientious, too intensely religious, too concerned about doing everything just the right way. But Wesley had a genius for administration, and Oglethorpe may have been one of the first to recognize it. He noted the quality of attention to the most minute detail that characterizes an outstanding administrator.

The governor desperately needed John. With him at his side and available to take over during his absences, Oglethorpe could feel more confident in his difficult task.

True, John could do with a little humanizing. He was altogether too otherworldly. Possibly marriage was the answer. Oglethorpe recalled that Wesley seemed to be attracted to Sophia Hopkey, and she was always at the church services gazing up at him with a certain look on her face. And they were frequently seen together.

Oglethorpe pondered the situation. It seemed to him that Wesley did not realize Sophia was a woman. Apparently he saw her only as a friend or companion. Some action must be taken to fuse these two separate personalities. Possibly if John married Sophia, he would settle in the colony on a permanent basis, and the responsibilities of married life would help him to more realistically face the frailties of human flesh.

And so the governor began to plan, and at ten o'clock one Sunday evening he sent for Wesley. Smiling as he welcomed him, he said, "I understand Miss Sophia's friend Miss Fosset is being married tomorrow morning. I have been concerned about Miss Sophia for some time. As you know, we are liable to be under Spanish attack at any time, and I don't want single girls exposed to this danger. Now that Miss Fosset is being married I think it best that Miss Sophia should return to Savannah. I have arranged with Mr. Houston for her to leave on the boat tomorrow morning. Please tell Miss Sophia about the arrangement."

John hurried off to break the news. Sophia was deeply disturbed, having absolutely no desire to return to Savannah and the Causton house. John tried to reassure her. After all, Causton had promised that he would do anything to help Miss Sophia.

At the improbable hour of six on Monday morning, John, decked out in his canonicals, officiated at the wedding. Sophia in wide-eyed innocence stood at her friend's side, listening to John's cultured voice, ". . . matrimony which is an honorable estate instituted of God."

"Did the words mean anything to him personally?" she wondered. Perhaps he was offering his explanation, ". . . is not by any to be entered into unadvisedly, or lightly, but reverently, discreetly, advisedly, soberly." Surely he had been discreet for long enough.

After the wedding they all adjourned to the newly erected Weston house. Located in the North Ward, it overlooked the parade ground where the soldiers drilled daily. Admiring the furniture of the new house, Sophia pointed out features to John, but he had little appreciation for household arrangements.

John hummed a hymn tune as he walked up Broad Street later that morning. He, too, was to travel to Savannah, but he would sail in the sloop while Sophia would make the trip in Mr. Houston's boat. When he called at the governor's house for letters, Oglethorpe handed over the packets and then said, "Oh, Mr. Wesley, the sloop isn't going to make the Savannah trip. You will have to sail in Mr. Houston's boat with Miss Sophia."

Elation struggled with apprehension. What a wonderful experience it would be to have Miss Sophia at his side for six days. But what might happen? This morning during the wedding ceremony he could not help but think about the possibility of marriage. His marriage. But he had soon pushed that dangerous thought aside.

In the methodical manner, which came so easily through constant usage, he began to sum up the pros and cons of the situation. After all, the governor had made the arrangements for the trip which threw them together. He had not planned the circumstances and could not be held responsible. John reminded himself of his own personal commitment to the celibate life. Now, as he felt the pressure, he once again spelled out his reasons for celibacy. None of these had changed.

He was reassured, moreover, as he recalled an earlier discussion with Sophia in which she told him she would never marry. John recalled her very words. If by some chance he weakened and asked her to marry him, she would stand by her resolution. So there was no need for him to really worry. John went about the preparations for the trip with a new calmness.

The boat sailed at noon. The governor had done his work well. There were no other passengers on the boat. John and Sophia sat alone in the passenger space, trying not to look self-conscious. A warm autumn sun shone down on them. Oars dipped rhythmically into the murky water, creaking rowlocks echoed a refrain. The lazy afternoon cast its hypnotic spell.

But John, determined not to be trapped, led off by reading aloud Bishop Patrick's prayer. Later in the afternoon he turned to Fleury's *History of the Church* for Sophia's edification. He piously hoped she would appreciate the magnificent example set by the ancient Christians who stood steadfast in their faith.

The afternoon flew, and all too soon John had to close his book and help Sophia ashore on the uninhabited island where they were to spend the night. After a warm meal, they stretched out to be lulled off to sleep by the sighing wind.

Early the next morning the boat got under way once more, pushing out across the Doboy Sound. Exposed to the open Atlantic, the waves came rolling in to mount their merciless attack on the small craft. In the midst of this struggle against wind and wave, John posed a theological question for his companion, "Miss Sophia, are you not afraid to die?"

She answered calmly, "No, I don't desire to live any longer. Oh that God would let me go now! Then I should be at rest. In the world I expect nothing but misery."

Sophia had learned her lesson well. Her answer showed she had the correct attitude towards this life. Her main hope was for the world to come.

At the end of the miserable day, wet and tired, they reached the southern tip of St. Catherines Island where they landed for the night. John watched Miss Sophia carefully. This girl, who for so long had lived such a sheltered life, was standing up admirably under the rigors of the trip. No word of complaint fell from her lips.

The roughness of the sea kept them marooned at St. Catherines for two days. Ever diligent in his responsibilities, John determined to make the most of the opportunity for widening Sophia's theological knowledge. Wednesday afternoon was given over to ethics and took the form of a long discussion of the subject, "Lying in order to do good." Sophia admitted that she had previously seen little wrong with the practice and confessed she had lied on occasions to John himself. However, John convinced her that this was wrong, and she promised never to do it again.

The following afternoon they walked to a part of the island sheltered from the blasting wind by a large bluff. He found a spot where they could sit comfortably, and they began to talk seriously about Christian holiness. Sophia knew very little about it, but with deadly earnestness sought to learn more of the Christian doctrine.

Although Friday morning brought continued darkened skies, the sailors decided to make a new attempt. Fierce winds clawed at the boat, and waves washing over the gunwale saturated passengers and crew, leaving them drenched and discouraged. But late that afternoon they had to give up and return to their departure point.

Again John saw it as a testing time for Sophia, but she came through with flying colors. The sight of this brave girl's willingness to suffer the adversities of the difficult situation set John to making a mental contrast between her unspoiled spirit and the generation of sophisticated females with whom he had so little patience. The more he saw of Sophia the better he liked her.

All hands set to work gathering wood. Soon an enormous fire drove away the chill and misery of the icy day at sea.

That night they spread the sail over four stakes and retired beneath the sheltering canvas. As John lay there, he found great difficulty in sleeping. He looked toward Sophia and saw that she too was awake.

"Miss Sophia, how far are you engaged to Mr. Mellichamp?"

"I have promised either to marry him or to marry no one at all."

In this dramatic moment Wesley heard himself impulsively saying, "Miss Sophia, I should think myself happy if I were to spend my life with you."

Sophia made the appropriate eighteenth-century response by bursting in tears and answering, "I am every way unhappy. I won't have Tommy; for he is a bad man. And I can have none else."

Relieved at first by her refusal, John saw the inequity of her ridiculous situation, especially when she said, "Sir, you don't know what danger you are in. I beg you speak no word on this head."

Silence fell. Sophia's mind was active. Would he accept the challenge? Perhaps she had stated the case too strongly.

"When others have spoken to me on the subject, I have felt an aversion to them. But I don't feel any to you."

All was set for a declaration. Lapping water, twinkling stars, and the black velvet backdrop of night. Sophia was waiting to be comforted.

But John had his answer. All this subtlety was beyond him. People meant what they said. The lady had spoken. She did not intend to marry anybody.

John broke the silence, "Let me read a psalm."

> Blessed is the man that hath not walked in the counsel of the ungodly, nor stood in the way of sinners, and hath not sat in the seat of the scornful.
>
> But his delight is in the law of the Lord; and in his law will he exercise himself day and night.
>
> And he shall be like a tree planted by the water side, that will bring forth his fruit in due season. . . .

They pushed on again on Saturday until the inclement weather forced them to take refuge on Bear Island. John and Sophia went off on a long walk. Inevitably conversation turned to Savannah and plans for the future there. Sophia burst into tears. With intense emotion she told John about her reluctance to return and live with the Caustons.

"I can't live in that house. I can't bear the shocks I meet there."

The worldly Caustons entertained a mixed group of friends and visitors. Sophia had seen and heard some shocking things. Should she go back to all this? Where else could she go?

"Don't be uneasy, Miss Sophia, on that account. If you don't care to be at Mr. Causton's, you are welcome to a room in our house . . ."

Was this a proposal? Sophia waited for him to continue.

"Or what I think would be best of all, and your aunt once proposed it, you may live in the house with the Germans."

There was nothing really personal in these recommendations. John was offering a refuge from a difficult situation. Not a home as she might have hoped. Sophia lapsed into silence.

The next day they set out again, and after one more night out, spent on Rattonpossom Island, they finally reached Savannah.

13.

A Narrow Escape

October 31, 1736–February 24, 1737

EVEN THOUGH SHE would have preferred not to go to the Causton home, Sophia could not find a better alternative and so she returned to live with her aunt. On the evening of her arrival Mr. Causton stopped in to see Wesley. He was really curious about how the romance had progressed while the two of them were in Frederica. Since Sophia had arrived she was mysteriously silent and uncommunicative. So he had come to Mr. Wesley.

Causton babbled on. Effusive in his gratitude, he told Mr. Wesley how much he appreciated all the efforts on behalf of his niece. He insisted that he knew so little about women and all he wanted was the best for Sophia. What would Mr. Wesley advise? Causton assured John he would do whatever was suggested.

John pondered the situation. He took Causton's remarks at face value. What would be the best for Miss Sophia? He finally made three requests. (1) In order that her education might continue she should come to the parsonage each morning and evening. (2) While she lived at Causton's home, Sophia should not be obliged to mix with their friends and visitors. (3) The name of Tom Mellichamp must never be mentioned in her presence.

Causton recoiled; it was not exactly the answer he expected. Was this conceited priest offering a gratuitous insult by saying the people they entertained were below Sophia's level in life? The restriction on Tom Mellichamp's name and the twice daily visits to the rectory had possibilities. It might still be that the priest would take the girl off his hands.

John, despite his awareness of the danger, spent long hours each day with Sophia. She came to Wesley's house for breakfast, after which he read *Hickes Devotions.* From eight to nine he taught her French. Then there was a break for prayers, and then back to the French again. And they spent each evening in study. And her visits were concluded with the reading of a psalm. But John continued to be ravaged by inner turmoil, as expressed in his diary, "I now begin to be much afraid. My desire and design are still to live single, but how long it will continue I know not."

Pastoral work kept him busy. Periodically he traveled to outlying settlements, including those of his German friends. Kind and considerate, long-suffering and deeply devout, he delighted in joining with them in singing their lovely hymns. They wove a spell over John that would ultimately lead him to certainty in his religious quest.

John's sense of justice turned him into a detective. A strange story lay behind Mr. Tailfer the Scotch surgeon, and John kept on the trail until he had gathered all the details. In a dramatic confrontation, with mingled feelings of satisfaction and disgust, John presented all the facts to the governor.

Tailfer while in Scotland had seduced the daughter of a relative, who, because she was pregnant and fearful of her father's wrath, agreed to immigrate with the surgeon to America.

The girl gave birth to her baby in Carolina, where Tailfer reduced her to the status of servant. In time the girl, miserable and depressed, developed a whining, whimpering manner which irritated the surgeon. But his cruel beatings and abuse only served to compound the problem.

Two years later she bore him a second child, but by this time he had met a woman he wanted to marry, so he sold the girl to an Indian trader.

Inwardly seething with indignation but trying to maintain a calm exterior as he presented the facts, Wesley was amazed when Tailfer freely admitted that most of the story was correct. However, the surgeon insisted that he had not sold the girl to the Indian trader but had given her to him.

Oglethorpe saw the utter futility of doing anything with as corrupt a character as Tailfer and ruled the girl must be released by the trader. He also decreed she must be given an allowance from public funds which would support her and the one surviving child. John left the depressing session, lamenting the treatment of women in a colony launched on the basis of such lofty ideals.

Tuesday, November 23rd, found him occupied with many tasks. A strange presentiment gripped him as he watched Governor Oglethorpe leaving the colony for England. The sight stirred the memories of the missionary aspirations with which he had left that country. They had never been fulfilled. Whatever Oglethorpe's shortcomings, he generally supported John and at least gave him a nominal backing in his missionary aims. But John had believed his mission to America was to convert the Indians. However, it seemed as if all he had done was arbitrate in petty squabbles and carry on the sort of ministry he could have exercised in any English village.

On Tuesday, December 28th, John and Delamotte decided they should again visit Frederica and set out on what was to be their last visit to the outpost. Deciding against the trip by sea because of winter weather, they mounted horses so as to make as much of the journey as possible across country.

The trip proved to be an arduous and interesting undertaking as they swam their horses across rivers, struggled through the dense forest, ran out of food, and had to resort to eating dried bear meat. John frankly noted in his diary that it was a wholesome though not very agreeable food.

Arriving at one little cluster of houses they received a hearty welcome. A young couple from an adjoining farm had planned to be married. The arrival of a minister seemed fortuitous to them. If John could remain a few hours, they would like him to officiate. Although a stickler for formalities, he was willing to forego calling the banns. Wearied by the rigors of the journey, John caught himself envying their settled life and mutual happiness.

On the second day of the new year they rode into Darien, the settlement of the sturdy Scotch Highlanders. Much more stolid and aggressive than the Germans, they were the fighters of the colony and did not have the same appeal to John. With a practical turn of mind they had only one church service a week, a fact which offended John. He believed that a man's spiritual status could be evaluated by the amount of time spent in spiritual exercises and a daily worship experience was minimal.

Since it was Sunday when John and Delamotte arrived in Darien, they attended that single weekly church service. Expecting the infrequent event would be something special, John was annoyed to discover that the preacher read his written sermon but offered the prayer extemporaneously. He observed in his diary, "Are not then the words we speak to God to be set in order at least as carefully as those we speak to our fellow worms?"

His comment on the Presbyterian minister was, "Mr. McLeod, their minister, is a serious, resolute and (I hope) prudent man."

Only twenty-five miles separated Darien from Frederica, but those miles were across water, and it finally took until Wednesday, January 5th, before they reached the fort.

The following Sunday Dr. and Mrs. Hawkins came to the church service Wesley conducted at Frederica. They remained behind to talk with him. John looked at them from a much better perspective now. In their company he strolled down a Broad Street sprouting with houses. Frederica was becoming a boom town. A boom which unfortunately would lead to an inevitable bust.

On the return trip to Savannah the awkward boat struggled against the contrary winds. A dark mist shrouded them for hours at a stretch, and John impatiently paced the deck of the ship, longing for the moment of reunion with Sophia. But when at last they arrived he found to his dismay that she had left Savannah to live with Mrs. Musgrove at Cowpen. The news bothered John. While the Indian woman undoubtedly needed help, he feared for what might happen to Sophia while living in such an untidy and badly kept house. Then, too, she would be exposed to the rough trappers who came to visit the Musgrove home.

Even though he was very tired, John immediately set out for Cowpen. When he arrived at the Musgroves' home, he took Sophia to one side and urged her to return with him to Savannah. She gathered her things, and they boarded a boat and sailed down the river that very evening. John could not help but note her willingness to cooperate with him.

In Savannah, Miss Bovey had become Sophia's close friend and constant companion. But it came as quite a surprise to John when Sophia told him Miss Bovey had decided to marry Mr. Burnside. He had some reservations about the match and hurried off to talk with Miss Bovey. Even though she listened with great respect, he could not convince her.

In discussing this later with Sophia, he explained that although he had some misgivings about the wedding, Miss Bovey had made up her mind and he was not going to raise any more objections. Even as he talked with Sophia, he realized the difficulty of her situation. In Frederica her best friend Miss Fosset had been married with John officiating. Now another close friend. One by one, her friends were marrying, but not her.

While taking a break from the daily French lesson, John and Sophia talked over the plans for Miss Bovey's wedding. He gradually slipped into it and suggested that marriage might really be a good idea for them. Sophia could hardly believe she was hearing the words for which she had yearned so long. But how strange are the ways of women. In her moment of triumph Sophia turned coquette, "But, Mr. Wesley, I have often heard you say a clergyman should never marry. And I am inclined to believe you are right. If a minister of the gospel becomes entangled in family responsibilities, how can he faithfully fulfill his ministry?"

She waited for his counter-argument. But this was one debate he was ready to lose. In his ambivalence of desire and fear, the old misgivings enveloped his mind. Sophia's teasing reply, instead of stimulating him, had provided a way of escape. Wesley, conscious of the danger to which he had exposed himself and gratefully aware of his escape, wrote in his diary, "I used no argument to induce her to alter her resolution."

The serious-minded minister began to cast around for help to bolster his bachelor resolve. The Moravians had always impressed him with their spiritual insights, so he approached their pastor, Mr. Toltschig. He listened intently to John's story and asked a number of penetrating questions. Then he dumbfounded Wesley by offering his opinion about marriage to such an attractive young lady, "I don't see why you should not."

Next, John asked the advice of Delamotte and Ingham. These bachelors gave the right answer. United with John in their Holy Club, they naturally did not want to lose their outstanding member. Obviously they brought all their masculine logic to bear in an effort to steer John from the pitfall of marriage.

When he told them about Mr. Toltschig's counsel, they reacted vehemently and hurried over to see the pastor, who in turn invited Moravian Bishop Seifart to join the discussion. John deliberately remained in his own house while his two closest friends, a Moravian bishop, and a Moravian pastor discussed his future.

Waiting patiently on through the evening, John finally decided at midnight that he should go over and enter the discussion. It had waxed warm with the group evenly divided—the Moravians for marriage, John's friends against it. Ingham led the attack on the proposal. "You do not know enough about her attitude to religion. She is putting on a good appearance, but we do not know if she is really sincere. There is a good chance she is just trying to get you to marry her."

John objected, "How can you say that? Only last Thursday when I mentioned marriage, Miss Sophia said she thought it best if a clergyman remained unmarried and that she herself didn't intend to get married."

"Oh yes," said Ingham in a sarcastic vein, "But you didn't make a direct proposal. If you were really to ask her to marry you, she would soon change her resolution."

John had no answer for this.

"You cannot make a sensible decision when you see her every day. Why don't you go out of town for a few days and give yourself a chance to take a fresh look at it all?"

John could see the logic of all this and immediately after church on Sunday evening he left town. And a somewhat surprised Sophia received a letter from John. It read, "I find, Miss Sophia, I can't take fire in my bosom, and not be burnt. I am retiring, therefore, for a while to desire the direction of God. Join me, friend, in fervent prayer, that He should show me what is best to be done."

For his retreat John had chosen a spot four miles from Savannah called Irene. He knew that Irene was the Greek word for peace and hoped that tranquility might replace his turmoil.

The next five days were full of uneasiness and unrest. In his diary he wrote the petition which he constantly reiterated, "Lord thou knowest! If it be best, let nothing be allowed to hinder, if not let nothing be allowed to affect it." As that black clad figure knelt in the corner of his room, he felt as if God had hidden his face. The righteous Lord of heaven had deserted him and given him over to his own sensual desires.

He interspersed the long periods of prayer with a feverish activity, visiting people, cutting pathways through the woods, reading aloud, singing. But as time passed, his resolution weakened, and on Tuesday he found a pretext to return on an errand to Savannah. When he got back to Irene, he wrote of his experience in his diary, "There I stayed about an hour; and there again I felt, and groaned under the weight of, an unholy desire. My heart was with Miss Sophia all the time. I longed to see her, were it but for a moment. And when I was called to take boat, it was as the sentence of death; but believing it was the call of God, I obeyed." At the end of five days he had accomplished nothing and eagerly hurried back to Savannah and Sophia.

But John continued to agonize and pray about his decision and finally concluded that there were two "mighty reasons" why he should not marry. (1) If he married it would obstruct his original intention of going out as a missionary to the Indians. (2) He felt he was not strong enough to bear the complicated temptations of married life.

We have a record of John's inner thoughts in his journal, but we know nothing of Sophia's reaction. What did she think of this bumbler as he periodically mentioned marriage and then backed off?

As they sat eating their morning meal at the rectory on Tuesday, February 15th, Sophia dropped a bombshell, "People wonder what I can do so long at your house; I am resolved not to breakfast with you any more. And I won't come to you any more alone."

John just sat and stared at Sophia. He could not believe his ears. The last time she would breakfast with him! He could not bear to even think about it and threw himself into a day of feverish activity. His busy pen worked on letters to the trustees, the rector of Lincon College, and Dr. Cutler. He then turned to updating his diary, meditated by reading Kempis, and took a long walk.

The following morning brought a sense of relief when he saw Sophia present for morning prayers. Following the benediction she let him know she intended to stand by her decision. And as a silent disappointed John stood looking dolefully at her, she added yet another sting, "I don't think I should come for French lessons any longer. But my uncle and aunt as well as I, will be glad of your coming to our house as often as you please."

Causton's house! "You know I don't love a crowd, and there's always one there."

Sophia smiled, "But we needn't be in it," and turned to walk away.

John became the pursuer. He found a different Sophia when he called at Causton's. Irritable and irascible, she seemed not to want to talk with him. When he tried to discuss her spiritual condition, she argued with him. His docile Sophia had been replaced by a shrew. Her change of attitude puzzled John. At the end of an hour, bewildered and confused, he prepared to leave.

Sophia wavered. It wouldn't do to part this way. So she carefully explained that she had been ill and that is what caused her to act as she had. And John was completely taken in.

14.

Helpers

February 24–March 8, 1737

AT THE NEXT MEETING of the Holy Club they discussed their need for reinforcements to help their mission work. With the departure of Charles their members had been reduced by one-fourth. The best arrangement seemed for one of their number to make the trip to England to enlist new recruits.

Just five days after the encounter with an irascible Sophia, John called again to see her. He told her of the group's decision that one of them should make the trip to England. He might be the one to go. A strange intensity came into her lovely eyes as she murmured, "If you are going to England, I have no tie to America left."

That night, following evening prayers, as they walked along

the road from John's house, he reopened the discussion, "Miss Sophia, what did you mean this afternoon by saying if I went to England you had no tie to America left?"

She burst into tears, "You are the best friend I ever had in the world."

Sunday brought a crowd of visitors to the parsonage, and among them was Sophia. John kept up conversation with his callers, but was fearful that she might leave before he could talk with her. One by one they left until only he, Delamotte, and Sophia remained.

Would that idiot never go? Finally, he got the hint. John and Sophia were alone. After all his waiting the moment had arrived, but John's usually orderly mind was utterly confused. He was at a loss for words and his heart was beating like a sledge hammer.

The surest way of getting his excitement under control was to talk to her about her spiritual condition. He tried and she gave him her full attention, but John felt himself slipping. When he reached over and took her hand, she made no effort to withdraw. Why not ask her to become engaged to him?

A thousand thoughts tumbled through his agitated mind. Then one memory came vivid and clear. She had told him her resolve never to marry. What right did he have to doubt her sincerity?

Finally the silence was broken by Sophia. "Mrs. Causton will be worrying about me. I must go."

Half relieved and half mad with himself, Wesley helped her on with her coat and told her goodby at the door.

He saw her every day during the next week, and each evening brought its mental torment. A dozen times he toppled on the brink but proudly wrote in his journal, "I touched her not."

His bachelor friends watched with apprehension and horror

as Wesley flitted in and out of a potential venture into matrimony. They talked amongst themselves as to what should be done.

Each evening following the lesson John walked Miss Sophia home. He braced himself for those nightly ventures remembering the biblical statement of its most infamous character, "Judas went out and it was night." Would the darkness of a Georgian night make him into an unfaithful servant who betrayed his calling?

On Thursday evening when John returned to the parsonage he found a very agitated Mr. Delamotte waiting for him. "I am afraid we must part. I don't see how I can possibly live in the same house when you are married to Miss Sophia."

John immediately reasserted his commitment to celibacy, "I have no intention of marrying her."

"You say that, but you don't know your own heart. I see clearly that you will soon be married unless you break off all relations with her. You should make up your mind as soon as possible. You are losing ground daily."

Painfully aware of the truth of what was said, John agreed to a conference with Ingham and Delamotte. After a preliminary discussion Ingham produced his journal. He opened it to Monday, November 3, 1735, and began to read.

> In the name of God Amen.
>
> We whose names are underwritten being fully convinced that it is impossible to promote the work of God among the heathen without an entire union amongst ourselves, or that such an union should subsist unless each one will give up his single judgment to that of the majority, do agree by the help of God.
>
> 1. That none of us will undertake anything of importance, without first proposing it to the others.
>
> 2. That whenever our judgments on indivinations differ, anyone shall give of his single judgment or indivination to the others.

3. That in case of an equality after begging God's direction the matter shall be decided by lot.

J.W., C.W., B.J., C.I.

At the conclusion of the reading John sat in a state of shock. He had temporarily forgotten the agreement, especially the way in which they had agreed to discover the will of God. In their present problem, point number three seemed to be the only solution.

In reading through the Bible John had noted that in the early church the disciples, faced with the difficulty of finding a successor to Judas, had cast lots and selected Mathias. And in the agreement from which Ingham now read they had bound themselves to this method of discovering God's will.

Following a period of fasting and prayer, they wrote upon three pieces of paper, "Marry," "Think no more of it this year," and "Think of it no more."

After earnest prayer, Delamotte drew the fateful piece of paper and read, "Think of it no more."

God had spoken. Wesley surrendered to the divine edict. He must not marry.

To help with the weakness now so noticeable in their leader, the Holy Club made another provision. Should John even see Sophia again? They decided to seek divine guidance.

The Almighty was given the choice of three propositions, "See her," "See her no more," "Only in the presence of Mr. Delamotte."

This time Ingham drew the paper. "Only in the presence of Mr. Delamotte."

In an ambivalence of sorrow on one hand and a sense of security on the other, John realized he was to be spared the temptation of being alone with Miss Sophia again.

Back in his room and away from his friends John fell to his knees in prayer. Long minutes passed before he could address the God who had made such demands upon a faithful follower. When the words finally came, the prayer was so vivid that he later wrote it into his journal.

"O Lord God, Thou God of my fathers, plenteous in mercy and truth, behold I give Thee, not thousands of rams or ten thousands of rivers of oil, but the desire of my eyes, the joy of my heart, the one thing upon earth which I longed for! O give me Wisdom, which sitteth by Thy throne, and reject me not from among Thy children!"

He gritted his teeth as he wrote, "I saw and adored the goodness of God, though what he required of me was a costly sacrifice."

15.

Wedding Bells

March 8–12, 1737

TUESDAY, MARCH 8, WAS A DAY John Wesley would never forget. He didn't know it, but he actually stood on the eve of his Gethsemane.

Miss Sophia and Miss Bovey attended evening prayers. At the conclusion of the service Sophia remained behind to ask John if he would call on Mrs. Causton. Without mentioning the cause of her distress, Sophia let John know that her aunt was terribly upset.

Wesley hastened to the Causton home. The maid met him at the door and ushered him in. Mrs. Causton, eyes red from weeping, made a dramatic entrance brandishing a letter in her hand. She thrust the missive into his hand, "Read it, Mr. Wesley. Read it."

Skimming through it, John saw the letter addressed to Sophia had come from Tom Mellichamp. It was the same sort of demanding intemperate writing, but it contained nothing that he had not stated many times before. Obviously the fact of the communication worried Mrs. Causton more than its contents. John tried to comfort the distraught woman. Things might not be as bad as they seemed.

Mrs. Causton seemed to enjoy John's attention, but when Sophia entered the room, she turned on her and spewed out a stream of bitterness, closing with, "Get out of my house; I will be plagued with ye no longer."

John became involved in the tirade when she said, "Mr. Wesley, I wish you would take her, take her away with ye."

"Miss Sophia is welcome to my house and anything that I have," stammered out the embarrassed John.

He left the house with a heavy heart. But not half as heavy as it might have been if he had seen another visitor who came that night to visit the Caustons.

John slept badly. At ten the next morning he set out again for the Causton home. Fussy Mrs. Causton welcomed him, then launched into a speech of gratitude for all that he had done for both Miss Sophia and her.

With the memory of the previous evening's events in mind, John wondered what she was talking about.

Then came the bombshell, "Miss Sophia desires you would publish the banns of marriage between her and Mr. Williamson on Sunday."

Mrs. Causton paused, surveying John with a gleaming eye, "Sir, you don't seem to be well-pleased. Have you any objection to it?"

"Madam, I don't seem to be awake. Surely I am in a dream."

Mrs. Causton played her role to the hilt. At last she had triumphed over this psalm singing priest who had spoken so insolently about her home.

"They agreed on it last night between themselves after you had gone. And Mr. Williamson asked Mr. Causton's and my consent, which we gave him."

Mrs. Causton paused to see the effect of all this on him, "But if you have any objection to it, pray speak. Speak to her. She is at the Lot. Go to her. She will be very glad to hear anything Mr. Wesley has to say. Pray go to her and talk to her yourself."

John made an effort to regain his composure, "No, if Miss Sophia is engaged, I have nothing to say."

He rose unsteadily to his feet as if to leave. Mrs. Causton urged him not to go. The rain pelted down outside, and John knew the only sensible line of action was to remain until it cleared.

John struggled to think clearly. What should be his attitude? By now he realized the Caustons were trying to marry Sophia off to him. He resented their attitude and had determined not to be manipulated by them. Was Mrs. Causton using this moment to provoke him into taking some drastic action? He had no intention of being pushed into a corner by the Caustons, but what of Sophia? He abhorred the thought of her throwing herself away on a man like Williamson. The only way to save her from such a horrible match might be to marry her himself. But he couldn't do that. God had already spoken on that matter. Sophia had a right to make her own decisions. If she had made up her mind to marry Williamson, John didn't want her. Let Williamson have her.

Finally, the rain stopped, and John, who had mentally left Mrs. Causton thirty minutes before, now hurried back to his house. He sat at the table where he had spent so many hours, hoping to regain his composure, but thoughts tumbled through his mind like acrobats, leaving him dizzy and dismayed.

Jumping up, he walked to the corner of the room and fell on his knees. But God seemed so far away—too far away to be concerned with his struggle.

The arrival of Delamotte brought an end to the unprofitable session of prayer. Perhaps he should go and talk with Sophia. That was what Mrs. Causton had suggested. But would it embarrass her?

He turned to the startled Delamotte, "Please go to Caustons' Lot and ask Miss Sophia if my company would be agreeable to her."

When Delamotte had gone, John lapsed again into deep depression. How could a man find the will of God? Prayer had accomplished nothing. He took up his Bible. He let the pages fall open at random, placed his finger on the page, "Blessed be thou of the Lord, my daughter; for thou hast showed more kindness at the latter end than at the beginning."

He tried again but the words were just as inapplicable. Even God had deserted him.

Delamotte returned; Miss Sophia would be happy to see him. John left the house immediately, and as he hurried along, he tried in vain to bring his tumbling thoughts under control. What would he say to Sophia when he saw her?

When at last he entered the gate of Causton's plantation, he was as confused as when he left home. But reality replaced conjecture when he unexpectedly came upon Sophia and Williamson sitting on a bench in the garden.

Williamson exuded confidence. "I suppose you know that it was agreed on last night between Miss Sophia and me."

In his misery John answered, "I have heard something; but I could not believe it unless I should hear it from Miss Sophia herself."

Sophia confirmed the news, "Sir, I have given Mr. Williamson my consent—unless you have anything to object."

John's heart raced. What did she mean? Was it possible she was saying, ". . . unless you will marry me"? No it couldn't be. If Sophia had meant that, she would have said it.

"If you have given your consent, the time is past; I have nothing to object."

Williamson, feeling confident at this reply, left them to talk things out.

But John had fallen into a state of shock. In his frustration and agony he lashed out at Sophia, "You told me you would never marry anyone except a religious man. Do you think Mr. Williamson is truly religious?"

Sophia answered defiantly, "I have no proof to the contrary."

"That is not enough. Before you staked so much on it, you should have had positive proof that he was religious."

The conversation continued with verbal shadow-boxing until it was interrupted by Williamson's return.

Noting her fiance's approach, Sophia said, "I hope I shall always have your friendship."

"I can still be your friend, though I should not stay in America."

"I hope you won't leave us."

Williamson now stood at their side. John addressed himself to both of them, "Assist each other in serving God with all your strength."

He turned to Sophia, "Remember the many instructions and advices I have given you."

In an impulsive gesture he embraced Williamson. Then in parting he did something he had never been able to do before. He held Sophia for a moment and felt a searing heat as he gently brushed his lips across her cheek.

John returned home to his beloved garden. An agonizing sense of loss gripped him, "I walked up and down, seeking rest but finding none. From the beginning of my life to this hour I had not known one such as this. God let loose my inordinate affection upon me, and the poison thereof drank up my spirit. I was stupid as if half awake, and yet in the sharpest pain I ever felt. To see her no more: that thought was as the piercings of a sword; it was not to be borne, nor shaken off. I was weary of the world, of light, of life."

Sophia Christiana Hopkey became Mrs. Williamson on March 12, 1737. They didn't wait for the banns to be called by Wesley but ran off with Miss Bovey and Mr. Burnside to Purrysburg in South Carolina for the wedding.

16.

Strangely Warmed

THE SILENT, BLACK CLAD FIGURE, bag in hand, with cloak wrapped close against the penetrating cool of evening, moved furtively through Savannah's unlit streets, avoiding houses that spewed out a tell-tale shaft of light which might betray his presence. He welcomed the dark clouds that blanketed the sky, dreading a moment when a sudden rift might unleash the full light of the December moon.

As he approached the river's edge, his eyes, now accustomed to the darkness, were able to distinguish the head of the rough-hewn wooden stairs that descended to the Savannah River flowing below. A man, obviously waiting for him, emerged from the darkness to whisper instructions as he took the bag and pointed down the stairs.

A precarious descent led to the gangplank across which a sailor helped him, and the dark clad man was led to the warmth of the cabin below.

A whispered command, the swish of a rope dropping into the water, the creaking of poles pushing out from the wharf, and the clumsy craft moved out to the middle of the stream.

Thus John Wesley left America seeking to avoid apprehension. The grand jury, under the influence of the Chief Magistrate Thomas Causton, had returned a series of true bills against Wesley accusing him of holding church services at the wrong hour, refusing to baptize except by dipping, withholding communion from certain people, most notably, Mrs. Williamson nee Hopkey.

The ministry that Wesley had begun with such high hopes had ended in disaster. He had traveled to America to convert the heathen, but he came to believe that he was not converted himself. And in many ways the imbroglio around the person of Sophia Hopkey dramatized what he saw as the barrenness of his spiritual life.

Perhaps Sophia Hopkey was also the key to the experience for which he looked. Just four months after he left America, Wesley sat down at Oxford and wrote a long letter to his mother. This lengthy epistle was in praise of Sophia, and in it he tacitly acknowledged that his attitude toward the girl had been wrong—he was making a most intimate confession of his failure to the most significant person in his life—his mother.

He also helped to found a "little society"—a group of like-minded people in which the basis of membership was the purpose, "To confess our faults one to another." Doubtless to them he told the whole story of his failure and ineptness in his relationship to Sophia.

Shortly after came the experience which he had sought for so long. He described it: "In the evening I went very unwillingly to a society in Aldersgate Street, where one was reading Luther's preface to the *Epistle to the Romans.* About a quarter before nine, while he was describing the change which God works in the heart through faith in Christ, I felt my heart strangely warmed. I felt I did trust in Christ, Christ alone for salvation; and an assurance was given me that He had taken away my sins, even mine, and saved me from the law of sin and death."

John Wesley's American ministry was launched on Sunday, March 7, 1736. The lesson for the day was 1 Corinthians 13, Paul's immortal Hymn to Love, a statement without equal in the whole of English literature. The subject of Wesley's first sermon was love, agape love, the love that gave, God's love.

The conclusion of Wesley's American ministry centered around love. Human love. A pathetic experience that crowded out his own good sense, led a girl into a foolish marriage and sent him back across the Atlantic with a sense of frustration and failure.

In the long look of history Wesley was to find the most productive extension of his work in America. In this new land his followers were to be more numerous than in any other country. Here too, Methodism was to adopt a unique episcopal form of government. But in his own mind his stay in America must have been completely overshadowed by the way in which he had loved and lost Sophia.

Sophia Hopkey, the first great love of Wesley's life, would have made him an excellent wife. She shared his religious convictions, was well-to-do and probably would have raised a fine group of children. They might have settled on one of her properties, and John, as a landed clergyman, would have continued as the rector of Savannah. His interest in gardening might have made him into an enlightened plantation owner. One among many of the colonial aristocracy.

Instead he lived a life in which he was continually short of money, in part because he placed little value on it. He was lonely because he feared a wife might hinder his preaching activities, and he was a restless itinerant in a life which kept him from the type of home life he loved so well.

The "Happy Traveler" one biographer calls him. He traveled the length and breadth of England, Scotland, and Ireland. But as he traveled he preached, and his preaching formed the foundation of the Wesleyan Revival which changed the hearts of English people and probably saved that country from a blood bath similar to the catastrophic upheaval across the channel, known to history as the French Revolution.

A beautiful portrait of Wesley in his old age shows his crest in the corner inscribed with his favorite verse, "God is love." That theme overshadowed all his ministry, but in a large measure because his experiences of earthly love were so unsatisfactory. A psychologist might say he sublimated his love for woman into a love for mankind. Wesley's loss became humanity's gain as he ministered to the whole household of faith.

The Frederica River meanders through the maze of swamp lands along coastal Georgia. St. Simons Island on the east, marshes and coast on the west. Over a century after John Wesley's disappointed departure from the royal colony another man came to that coastal area.

A native born Georgian and graduate of Oglethorpe College, he was the nineteenth-century fruit of that idealistic settlement in the new world.

His ready pen put on paper an interpretation of his native Georgia. Poetry that sang they said. In time he was to become Georgia's most illustrious poet.

A great oak now stands on a swarth of land dividing two modern highways. Under that oak in the year 1870 sat Sidney Lanier looking toward the distant Fort Frederica across the marshes of Glynn. Entranced by the wide sweep of these marshes, he saw not swamp land but a mute message of the Creator.

As the marsh-hen secretly builds on the watery sod,
Behold I will build me a nest on the greatness of God:
I will fly in the greatness of God as the marsh-hen flies
In the freedom that fills all the space 'twixt the marsh and the skies;
By so many roots as the marsh-grass sends in the sod
I will heartily lay me a-hold on the greatness of God:
Oh, like to the greatness of God is the greatness within
The range of the marshes, the liberal marshes of Glynn.

The greatness of God! John Wesley wanted to apprehend that above everything else, and he felt that to get it he must renounce all earthly loves, particularly that of Sophia Hopkey.

But there were moments, such as when he wrote of Sophia Hopkey, ". . . she was such a companion as I never expect to find again should I live a thousand years . . ."

Other Books of Interest by John Drakeford

THE AWESOME POWER OF THE LISTENING EAR

It would be very proper to subtitle this volume "How to win friends, make money, build a career—in fact, do almost anything you want to do—by learning how to listen."

The Awesome Power of the Listening Ear has many implications for those in religious vocations, but is not at all specifically limited to the religious market. The medical doctor, the psychiatrist, the school teacher, the businessman, the young man or woman in love—any one of these people can use and profit from this very practical book.

John Drakeford draws heavily from his experience as a practicing listener in a counseling center on the campus of a large seminary.

Here are some of the subjects that will fascinate and benefit the reader—

Work on your listening inertia
Listening without ears
Listen for the sound of silence
Consider your listener's perspective
Cultivate the skill of reply
Ask a question but do it carefully

FORBIDDEN LOVE

A Homosexual Looks for Understanding and Help

Jeff Johnson was a music director in a local church and he was a homosexual.

Forbidden Love is painfully frank; it is agonizingly personal; and it is depressingly true. Jeff traces his background from childhood up to and including his arrest and confinement in prison. He describes his feelings and reactions when he is left completely alone—his wife and his children desert him when the awful truth becomes public knowledge. His search for help and understanding reveals a great wasteland where compassion and involvement should have dwelt.

Every "straight" adult needs to read this book. The Christian will find himself head-on with the responsibility of coming to grips with the real meaning of redemption. The church cannot limit or discriminate when it dispenses grace.

Forbidden Love is the story of human struggle. To divorce oneself from the realities of existence and hope that the problems will quietly go away is to deny man's potential for fulfillment. Jeff Johnson's story evokes and articulates every man's involvement with every other man. If some of the facts are frightening, if some of the information he divulges is disgusting, it is nevertheless true. You owe him the opportunity to be heard.

John Drakeford became acquainted with him when Jeff came to Integrity Therapy seeking help. Dr. Drakeford says, "Jeff and I spent many hours in conference. The interviews were taped and what we have in this book is his perception of the unusual events that transpired during the first forty years of his life. It is his story and I have tried to let him tell it 'like it is.' "

THIS INSANITY CALLED LOVE

This insanity called love?
How else would you define an emotion that

obsesses its victims
immobilizes them
distorts their judgment
subjects them to delusions
sends them on a never-ending quest to find the love-object ideal?

Through the eyes of a practical psychologist marriage counselor, Dr. Drakeford looks at the romantic love experiences of six striking personalities. Separated in time by centuries and in background by bewilderingly diverse circumstances, religion was a pervading element in the lives of all of them. And because—or in spite of—their encounters with romantic love, all of them added new and positive values to society in general.

An informative, entertaining, often humorous, but above all, perceptive study of a subject that has intrigued man throughout history, here is a new slant on

Eleanor of Aquitaine
The Medieval Emily Post

Martin Luther
The Monk Who Married a Nun

John Wesley
Lover on Horseback

Benjamin Disraeli
"My Dear Dizzy"

David Livingstone, who left his heart in Chitambo's Village

Anton Boisen, who climbed out of the depths, to help his fellow-man